113- $5-

Around the Corner

REVISED EDITION

- **ODILLE OUSLEY**
- **DAVID H. RUSSELL**

GINN AND COMPANY | BOSTON · NEW YORK · CHICAGO · ATLANTA
DALLAS · PALO ALTO · TORONTO · LONDON

Acknowledgments

Grateful acknowledgment is made to the following authors and publishers for permission to use and adapt copyrighted materials:

Abingdon-Cokesbury Press for "The Seven Little Piffles" from *The Seven Little Pifflesniffs* by Margaret Stimson Richardson, copyright 1952 by Pierce and Smith, and published by Abingdon Press.

Artists and Writers Guild, Inc. for "Casey Joins the Circus" by Dorothea F. Dobias, copyright 1936; used by permission of the copyright owners, Artists and Writers Guild, Inc.; and for "Little Pond in the Big Woods" from *Little Pond in the Woods*, a Little Golden Book by Muriel Ward, copyright 1948 by Simon and Schuster, Inc., and Artists and Writers Guild, Inc., adapted by permission; and for "Dolly" by Elizabeth Coatsworth, from *Horse Stories*, a Big Golden Book by Elizabeth Coatsworth and Kate Barnes, copyright 1954 by Simon and Schuster, Inc., and Artists and Writers Guild, Inc.

Dorothy W. Baruch, the author, for "Big Fellow and the Airfield" from *Big Fellow at Work*, copyright 1930.

Erick Berry, the author, and *Child Life* magazine for "The Little Farm in the Big City."

Basil Blackwell & Mott, Ltd., for the poem "The Rabbit" from *Fifty New Poems for Children* by E. L. M. King.

Charles Scribner's Sons for "The Hollyberrys at the Shore," adapted from *The Hollyberrys* by Alice Dalgliesh and Cleo Bennett; copyright 1939 by Charles Scribner's Sons. Used by permission of the publishers; and for "Two Horses," adapted from *We All Go Away* by Lavinia R. Davis; copyright 1940 by Charles Scribner's Sons. Used by permission of the publishers.

Doubleday & Company, Inc., for "Airplane Andy" adapted from *Airplane Andy* by Sanford Tousey, copyright 1942 by Sanford Tousey, reprinted by permission of Doubleday & Company, Inc.

Carroll Lane Fenton, the author, and *Children's Activities* magazine for "Mother Blacktail and Her Twins."

Carolyn Forsyth, the author, for "Something to Think About," reprinted by special permission from *Jack and Jill*, copyright 1952 by The Curtis Publishing Company.

Alice Gall and Fleming Crew for "Bushy Tail" from *Bushy Tail*, copyright 1941 by Oxford University Press, Inc.

2

Harper & Brothers for "Fourth Floor" from *I Live in a City* by James S. Tippett, copyright 1927 by Harper & Brothers.

Lucien Harris, Manager of the works of Joel Chandler Harris, for "Mr. Rabbit, Rain-maker," from *Tales of Uncle Remus* by Joel Chandler Harris.

Leroy F. Jackson for permission to use the poem "How a Puppy Grows," from *Jolly Jingle Book* by Leroy F. Jackson.

Alice Geer Kelsey, the author, and The Methodist Publishing House for "Red Roofs, Green Roofs" from "Red Roofs and Green Roofs" in *Pictures and Stories*, October 1952.

Lothrop, Lee & Shepard Company for "The Flying Firemen," from *Sky High* by Edith Thacher Hurd.

Berta Metzger, the author, and Oxford University Press, Bombay for "The Boy and the Door" from "The Servant and the Door" first published in *Tales Told in India* by Oxford University Press, Bombay, copyright 1935.

Melita Meyer, the author, for "Hoppy, the Helicopter" used with permission of *Jack and Jill*, copyright 1952 by The Curtis Publishing Company.

Lilian Moore, the author, and *Humpty Dumpty's Magazine* for "Ben and the Ball Game" from "The Big Game."

Mariquita Mullan, the author, and *Jack and Jill* for "Johnny and Teeny" from "Jackson and Teenie," adapted by special permission from *Jack and Jill*, copyright 1954 by The Curtis Publishing Company.

Thomas Nelson & Sons for "The Little Old Woman and the Baby Elephant" from *More About the Little Old Woman Who Used Her Head* by Hope Newell.

Oxford University Press, Inc., for "Across the River," adapted from *Flat Tail* by Alice Gall and Fleming Crew copyright 1935 by Oxford University Press, Inc.; and for "Chris" from *Chris* by Kay Bishop, copyright 1946 by Oxford University Press, Inc. Used by permission.

The Platt & Munk Company, Inc., for "David's Silver Dollar" by Elizabeth R. Squires; and for "Mary Ann's Ticket" from *Sally Goes to the Circus Alone* by Louise Eppenstein, published as special arrangements with the publishers, The Platt & Munk Company, Inc.

Miriam Clark Potter, the author, and *American Childhood* for "Mrs. Goose and the Strange People" from "Mrs. Goose's Strange Visitors."

G. P. Putnam's Sons for the poem "The Elephants" from *Hop, Skip, and Jump* by Dorothy Aldis, published by G. P. Putnam's Sons.

Rand McNally & Company for "The Little Woman Wanted Noise" from *The Little Woman Who Wanted Noise* by Val Teal, copyright 1943; and for "Timothy, the Little Brown Bear" from *Timothy, the Little Brown Bear* by Jane Flory, copyright 1949 by Rand McNally & Company, publishers.

Lilly Shutter, the author, and *Jack and Jill* for "Oscar and the Bus Driver," published by The Curtis Publishing Company.

Ruth Elizabeth Tanner, the author, and *Wee Wisdom* magazine for "Peter and the Pilot" from "Something Did Happen."

Miriam Young, the author, and *Story Parade* magazine for "The Wonderful Washing Machine."

3

Stories in This Book

We Live in a City

Circus Stories

All Around the City

Up and Away

4

We Live in a City

Here Comes the Parade!

Ben and Mary Ann ran
to the big front window.

" Here it comes ! " said Mary Ann.
" Here comes the balloon parade."

" Come and look, Joe ! " called Ben.
" Look at all the big balloons ! "

" What funny balloons ! " said Joe.
" Is the big duck a balloon, Ben ? "

" Yes, the big duck is a balloon,"
said Ben. " The rooster is a balloon, too."

8

The three children laughed
at the funny big balloons.

"Look at the big, big bunny!" said Joe.
"Here it comes now. See the big bunny
go hoppity-jump!"

"Here comes something funny,"
said Ben. "It looks like a donkey."

"It is a donkey," called Mary Ann.
"See the donkey go up and away."

"Oh, Mother," called Ben. "Hurry!
Come and see the balloon parade.
Here are some more balloons now."

9

Mother came to the window to look
at the balloon parade.

After the donkey came other balloons.

"I like the cowboy balloon!" said Ben.
"I like to see the cowboy's pony go
up and down. See him over there!"

Soon the cowboy balloon was gone.
All the other balloons were gone, too.

Around the corner went the last
of the funny big balloons.

10

Ben watched the last of the parade
go around the corner.

"Oh, Mother," he said. "May I follow
the parade? I want to see it again."

"I think we can see the balloon parade
on the TV," said Mother. "Let's turn it on
and find out."

Then the TV clicked. The children
watched to see what would come on.

Yes, there were the balloons again.

There was the balloon parade on TV.

11

"What a good surprise!" said Ben.
"Now we can all follow the parade.
We can follow it on TV."

The children sat down
and watched the parade on TV.

The bunny went hoppity-jump again.
The pony went up and down again.
The children laughed and laughed.

It was fun to watch the balloon parade.
Up and down the streets
and all over the city it went.

12

Boxes and Boxes

One morning Ben and Mary Ann
ran to Father.

"We are building a store at school,
Father," said Ben. "Can you help us
find some boxes, please?"

"Let's go to the basement," said Father.
"I have some empty boxes down there."

Ben and Mary Ann followed Father
down to the basement.

Father said, "You may have some
of the boxes in this corner.
Take as many as you want."

The children put some empty boxes
on Ben's express wagon. Then away
they went up the street to school.

"Look at the boxes!" called the man
in the shoe store as Ben came by.
"Do you want some more boxes?"

"Yes, please," said Ben. "We want
to build a play store at school.
We want all the boxes we can get!"

So the man in the shoe store put
two empty boxes on Ben's express wagon.

The man who worked at the fruit store
on the corner saw the boxes, too.
He put some more boxes on the wagon.

"Thank you," said Mary Ann. "Now
we will have a fine store at school."

14

Mr. Tony, the peanut man,
was at the corner of the block.

He had warm popcorn and peanuts
by the stove in his little wagon.

"See all our boxes, Mr. Tony!"
called Mary Ann. "We are going
to build a play store at school today."

"Boxes and boxes!" laughed Mr. Tony.
"What a fine load of boxes you have!
Here is one of my boxes for you."

Mr. Tony put a yellow box in the wagon.

"Thank you," called the children.

Then around the block
and on to school they went.

Soon Ben and Mary Ann were at school
with their load of boxes.
They saw many other children
with loads of empty boxes, too.

"Look at all the boxes!" said Miss Day.
"I think you have enough boxes now.
You may work on the store this morning."

The children all started to work
on the store in the corner.

Some of the children painted boxes
for the front of the store.

Some of the children painted signs
for the store.

16

Mary Ann picked up a little yellow box.
Rattle, rattle, rattle it went!

"Come here," called Mary Ann.
"This box has something in it."

The children stopped their work.
They all wanted to see what was
inside the yellow box.

"Look!" called Mary Ann. "Mr. Tony
put some peanuts in this little box."

"We can play store with the peanuts,"
said Dick. "It will be fun."

It was fun to play with the peanuts.
It was fun to eat the peanuts, too,
when lunch time came!

After lunch the boys and girls made up
a rhyme about the peanuts.

> Popcorn and peanuts,
> Warm and brown.
> Popcorn and peanuts,
> The best in town!

" This would make a good sign
for Mr. Tony's wagon," said Mary Ann.

" Let's paint a sign and take it
to Mr. Tony after school," said Ben.

That is just what they did. And
that is how Mr. Tony, the peanut man,
got his fine new sign.

18

At the Big Store

Joe liked to go to the big store
with Mother. He liked to look at the toys.
He liked to ride in the big elevators.

" We will get some balloons and candles
for Mary Ann's party," said Mother.
" Her birthday is coming soon."

" Here is the elevator," said Joe.
"Let's go up and see the toys now."

" We will get a toy today," said Mother.
" The toy will be a prize at the party."

19

"I will get the balloons and candles," said Mother. "You may look at the toys."

Joe wanted to find a toy that everyone would like. But there were many toys!

Joe looked at a toy fire truck.
He sat on a blue toy tractor.
Then he saw a toy telephone
and some big building blocks.

He stopped to bounce a rubber ball.
Bounce, bounce, went the rubber ball!
Joe saw many toys. Drums, boats, cars!

"I will look some more," said Joe.

He walked around the store
looking and looking and looking.

20

" Joe ! Where are you ? " called Mother.
" Where did you go ? "

" That's funny," said the man.
" He was right here. Where can he be ? "
Then the man laughed.

" Joe has found our big playhouse,"
said the man. " That's where he is.
He has found Sonny Bear too."

" Oh, Mother, may we take this toy bear
home with us ? " said Joe. " He can dance."

" Yes, he will make a fine prize,"
said Mother. " It will be fun
to see him dance at the party."

"Let's go down this way, Joe,"
said Mother. "We can ride down
to the next floor. We must hurry home
to lunch now."

Mother and Joe got on the stairs.
Just then Sonny Bear bounced
right out of Joe's hands.

Away Sonny Bear went. Down the stairs
he rolled. Bump! Bump! Bump!

Then Sonny Bear stopped. He stopped
and sat right up on one stair
until he came to the next floor.

"Sonny Bear is in a hurry to get
to his new home," said Mother. "I think
he is a toy everyone will like."

And do you know, Mother was right.
Everyone did like Sonny Bear.

22

Chris

Chris wanted to be a good little dog.
He did not make much noise.
He did not jump up on the chairs.

Chris liked to live with Mrs. Olds.
He liked to play right next door
with Ben and Mary Ann. But he did not
like to live in a city apartment.

"Come, Chris," called Mrs. Olds.
"We will go for a walk now."

Chris always came when he was called.
He liked to go out of doors.

But going for a walk in the city
was not much fun after all.

Chris wanted to run and bark
with the dogs along the way.

He wanted to run after the birds.

He wanted to stop and play
with his friend Mike, the paper boy.

He wanted to dig. How he liked to dig !

But Chris could not run and play
and dig. He could not bark much.

He had to walk along the sidewalk
with Mrs. Olds. Soon he was back
in the little apartment again.
24

How Chris wished something
would happen! He waited and waited.
Then one day something did happen.

Chris found the apartment door open.
Out of the door he went in a hurry.

Down the long hall he went.
Down the basement stairs and
out of the apartment house he ran.

It was a cold day and very soon
Chris was a cold, cold little dog.

But he was happy to be out of doors.

He ran this way. He ran that way.

He ran as fast as a long little dog
could run.

Chris saw a little girl
on Spring Street. She was waiting
for a bus with her mother.

The mother had a big gray muff. She
put the muff down and turned to help
the little girl with her mittens.

Chris saw the gray muff. He liked it.
He picked it up and away he ran.

Across the street and around the corner
Chris went. Faster and faster he ran!

What fun Chris had! He was playing
a game. But he was cold! Oh, so cold!

He saw an empty box on the sidewalk.
So into the box Chris went with the muff.

Chris looked at the muff. He barked
at it. Then he crawled right into it.

Soon night came and Chris went to sleep.

26

The next morning Chris heard a noise.

He looked out and saw his friend

Mike, the paper boy, on the corner.

"Papers! Papers!" Mike called.

"Get your papers here!"

Chris came out of the big box.

Mike laughed when he saw Chris.

Then Mike saw Mrs. Olds.

Mrs. Olds was out looking for Chris.

"Mrs. Olds!" called Mike.

"Here is your little dog, Chris."

She was very happy to see him again.

Chris was happy to see Mrs. Olds, too.

" Chris, you look funny in that muff ! "
said Mrs. Olds. " Where did you get it ?
Come along home with me now."

"I am not very busy, Mrs. Olds,"
said Mike. "I will walk home
with you and Chris."

Ben and Mary Ann laughed
when they saw how funny Chris looked.

Mike gave Mrs. Olds her paper
and said good-by to Chris. Then he
went back to Spring Street.

Mrs. Olds and Chris went right up
to their own warm apartment.

28

Mrs. Olds gave Chris his warm dinner.
Then she opened her paper. Mrs. Olds
was looking for something in the paper.
Soon she saw what she was looking for.

> LOST—Gray muff at Spring
> Street bus stop. Mrs. Mary
> Green. Telephone: AL 2-1347.

"Oh," said Mrs. Olds. "There it is!"
She went to the telephone and
called AL 2-1347. Soon she was talking
with Mrs. Green.

Mrs. Green was pleased to know
that her gray muff had been found.

29

Soon everyone was happy again.
Mrs. Green was happy because
she had her big gray muff again.

Mrs. Olds was happy because
Chris was at home again.

Chris was happy, too!
He had found out that his own
warm apartment was a good home
in the busy city.

It was a very good home
for a little dog named Chris.

So he never wanted to run away again.

30

A Birthday Surprise

The day of the birthday party came.
Mary Ann put on her new blue dress
and her new blue shoes.

Ben and Joe got dressed
for the party, too.

Sonny Bear was ready for the party.
Joe and Mary Ann put him
in a chair by the door.

"Your friends will be coming soon,"
called Mother. "Run to the window
and look for the Spring Street bus."

31

"The bus is here," called Joe.
"I can see Bob and Dick. I can see
the three girls, too. They are all
coming in now."

Bill was standing at the door
of the elevator as the children came in.

"Going up!" called Bill.

The children ran to the elevator.

"Call your floors, please," said Bill.

"Fourth floor, please," said the girl
with the pretty red mittens.

"Fourth floor," said the boy
in the brown coat and hat.

The other children wanted to get off
at the fourth floor, too.

Bill laughed.

"Here we go," he said.
"The fourth floor is the next stop.
It is a busy day up there.
Something must be going on."

32

Mary Ann opened the door
of Apartment 4A and looked out.

She saw five of her friends
get off the elevator.

Joe ran to the door with Mary Ann.

"Come in," called Joe. "Come in
and see Sonny Bear! He can dance!"

The children watched Sonny Bear dance.
They sang birthday songs. They told
funny stories.

Then they had a peanut race.
Nan found the most peanuts.

"Nan wins," said Mary Ann.
"She gets Sonny Bear for a prize."

Just then Mother came in with a
big birthday cake with candles on it.

33

Soon the party was over. Out of
Apartment 4A the children all came.

Mary Ann took some birthday cake
out to Bill.

"Thank you," said Bill. "I thought
something was happening up here today.
It has been busy on the fourth floor."

"I had a party," said Mary Ann.
"Today is my birthday. See the
little red candles on the cake!"

"Get in," said Bill. "I will take
the birthday party for a ride. I have
a surprise for you."

34

"We will take a ride all the way down to the basement," said Bill. "Here we go!"

"What is the surprise?" asked Ben. "Is the surprise in the basement?"

Bill stopped the elevator.

"We have some new neighbors," he said. "Just look over here."

The children followed Bill. They looked in a box in the corner. There they saw the new neighbors.

"Kittens!" said Dick and Bob.

"Mrs. Tabby Cat with five kittens!" said Mary Ann. "And look at the fine sign Bill has put on the box!"

Mrs. Tabby Cat and Family
Apartment 1A

35

Mrs. Tabby Cat and Family
Apartment 1A

Fourth Floor!

" Fourth floor ! "
Is what I say
When I come in
From play.

My home
Is on that floor.
It has a seven
On the door.

Six other doors
Are on our hall
With a different family
Behind them all.

James S. Tippett

Circus Stories

Casey Joins the Circus

Casey Sees the Baby Elephant

Casey was a little brown and white dog who had no home. He lived in the basement of an empty building.

One day the circus came to the city where Casey lived. So he ran out and watched the circus parade go by.

There were beautiful white horses in the parade. There were monkeys and many other animals in cages.

There were five big gray elephants. At the very last of the parade was a baby elephant walking beside his mother.

38

Casey liked the beautiful white horses. He liked the lions. He liked the other animals in the big cages, too.

Casey liked the baby elephant best of all. So he walked beside the baby elephant. Casey walked with him all the way back to the circus tents.

Casey stopped at the lions' cage. He watched the lions walking up and down.

Then Casey watched the monkeys as they climbed around in their cages. How the monkeys chattered and chattered!

Casey liked the funny monkeys. But he liked the baby elephant best!

Casey wished he could join the circus and stay with the baby elephant.

Casey wanted to see the baby elephant again. He found the elephants' tent and ran inside.

Just then Casey heard a noise outside. He saw the sides of the elephants' tent blow in and out.

"A storm!" thought Casey. Then he saw that the elephants were afraid of the storm.

Elephants are always afraid of storms if they are in a tent. They do not like to see the tent sides blow in and out.

Casey was not afraid of the storm. He was not afraid of the elephants.

40

How Casey Helped

Some of the elephants who were afraid started to run away. Casey helped the men get them back into the tent.

Soon the storm was over, and the elephants were not afraid any more.

But the baby elephant was gone!

The men went out to look for him. They looked all night long. But they could not find the baby elephant.

"What shall we do?" said a tall man. "The circus will not be the same if we do not find the baby elephant."

41

The next day the drums were playing. The circus was about ready to start. But the baby elephant was still gone.

"Look!" called one of the circus men. "Here comes the baby elephant. Here he comes across the field."

Then the circus men saw Casey. He was coming across the field with the baby elephant.

"The little dog is bringing the baby elephant home," said the tall man.

Casey took the baby elephant right to his place in the circus tent.

Then Casey sat down nearby. He wanted to stay near the baby elephant.

42

"That little brown and white dog likes elephants," said one of the circus men.

"He is the same dog who helped us with the elephants in the storm," said another man. "He was not afraid."

"We will keep him," said the man in the red coat. "We will keep him for our elephant dog. It is good to have a small dog in the elephants' tent. Then the elephants will not be afraid of other small animals."

"Yes, this little dog can join the circus," the men said. "He can be the elephants' dog and earn his way."

So that is how Casey happened to be the elephants' dog. And that is how he happened to join the circus.

43

Mary Ann's Ticket

Mary Ann, Ben, and Joe were at the circus with Father.

" Let's walk around in this tent and look at the animals first," said Father. " Then we will go into the big tent."

Mary Ann stopped to look at the lions. " Listen to them roar and roar," she said.

The boys liked to watch the monkeys playing in their cages. One funny little monkey was eating peanuts.

" It is about time for the circus to start," said Father. " Come along now."

44

"Oh look, Father!" called Mary Ann. "See all the cotton candy! May we have some, please?"

Father laughed. Then he gave the man some money. "We want some cotton candy, please," Father said.

The children took the soft cotton candy. Then they all started for the gate of the big circus tent.

"Here are your tickets," said Father. "Do not drop them. Give them to the man at the gate."

"This cotton candy is good," said Mary Ann. "But I want to see the circus now. Come on, let's hurry."

" Tickets ! Tickets ! Tickets, please ! " called the man at the gate.

Ben gave his ticket to the man and went in at once. The gate went click.

Then Joe gave his ticket to the man, and the gate went click again.

" Where is my ticket ? " said Mary Ann. " Where is it, Father ? I have lost it ! "

Just then a funny clown came running up. " What is the matter, little girl ? " he asked. " What is the matter ? "

Mary Ann turned around in a hurry.

" I do not have my ticket," she said. " I have lost it. I had it in my hand. Now I cannot find it."

Mary Ann turned to her father. " Oh, Father," she said. " What shall I do ? "

" Stop crying," said Father. " We will help you find your ticket. It must be right here somewhere ! "

46

Father looked for the circus ticket. The clown helped look for it, too. Then all at once the clown started to laugh.

" Why are you laughing, Mr. Clown ? " asked Mary Ann. " Do you see something that is funny ? "

" Yes, I do," said the clown. " I see something that is very funny ! I am laughing at your pink ticket. It is in a very funny place."

" My pink ticket ! " said Mary Ann. " Do you see it, Mr. Clown ? Please tell me where it is."

"Here it is," said the clown. "Your pink ticket is sticking to your pink cotton candy."

Mary Ann laughed with the clown. "Thank you very much for helping me find my ticket," she said.

Ben and Joe waved to Mary Ann.

"Come on, Mary Ann," called Ben. "The circus is going to start!"

There was one click of the gate and then another. Now Father and Mary Ann were in the big tent.

"Good-by!" called the clown. "Look for me in the big parade. I will wave to you, Mary Ann."

48

Here Come the Clowns!

Three circus clowns were dressing in a small tent. It was time for them to get ready for the big circus.

One clown was very big. One clown was very little. The other clown was very tall.

The three clowns were going to put on their funny-looking suits. They were looking in their big boxes. They were looking for trick hats and funny shoes.

The three clowns wanted to look as funny as they could for the big circus. They wanted to make the children laugh.

49

The big clown had on a green suit
with red and yellow dots on it. He had
on long green shoes.

The big clown painted a yellow nose
on his big white face. Then he put on
a long yellow coat.

"Now for my trick hat that bounces up
and down," said the big clown.

The trick hat was made of rubber. It
had a rubber sunflower on top of it.
The sunflower bounced up and down, too.

"This is the funniest hat I have,"
said the big clown. "I think the
children will like it." He waved to
the other clowns and went out with
Billy, his trick goat.

The tall clown was a policeman clown. He had on a policeman suit with big yellow buttons on the coat.

On one foot he put an old red shoe. On the other foot he put a long yellow shoe with buttons on it.

"Now for my green hair," he said. "This is the funniest hair I have. It always makes the children laugh."

The policeman clown got into his old car. The wheels were coming off, and the engine was steaming.

A pet duck sat by the clown's side. Away they went into the big tent.

51

The little clown was dressing, too. He painted his face white and put a big red dot on his nose.

He put on a funny cowboy suit and a big cowboy hat with pink feathers on it.

The cowboy clown had a funny little donkey with a long tail and long, long ears. The clown tied a funny trick hat on the little donkey's head.

"I hear the drums," said the cowboy clown. "It is time for the circus to start." And into the big circus tent he went with his little donkey.

52

Joe, Ben, and Mary Ann were in the big circus tent. They were eating their pink cotton candy. They had a bag of popcorn too.

" Here come the clowns ! " shouted Ben.

" Look, Father ! " called Mary Ann. " The clowns are coming this way."

First came the funny big clown with the sunflower hat on his head.

Then came the policeman clown in his funny old car. Another clown was in the funny old car with him.

Last of all came the cowboy clown with his funny little donkey.

53

"The big clown is the funniest one," shouted Ben. "See his sunflower hat jump up and down!"

"I see the clown who helped me find my ticket," said Mary Ann.

"He sees you, too, Mary Ann," said Father. "See him wave!"

"My clown is in the car with the policeman clown," shouted Mary Ann. "They are the funniest clowns of all."

"Look at the cowboy clown!" said Joe. "See his funny little donkey with the trick hat tied on his head. I think the cowboy clown is the funniest!"

"They are all funny," said Father.

The boys and girls in the big circus tent thought so, too. They laughed and laughed and laughed.

All the clowns were happy. They liked to make the children laugh.

54

The Little Old Woman and the Baby Elephant

Mother did not go to the circus with Mary Ann, Ben, and Joe. But at night when they went to bed, she told them this story.

Once there was a little old woman who lived in the country. One morning she saw a baby elephant running around in her garden. He was pulling up her cabbages and corn and beans.

" Oh, my!" she said. "I have never had a baby elephant in my garden before."

55

The Little Old Woman watched the baby elephant running around the garden.

She thought, " I must give him some hay. Then he will like the country."

So she gave the baby elephant some hay. But he went right on pulling up cabbages and eating them.

" He can get something to eat all right," said the Little Old Woman. " But I must find a house for him. He must have a roof over his head.

" He could live in the barn," said the Little Old Woman. " Then he could have the barn roof over his head.

" No," thought the Little Old Woman. " The goose and the duck would not like to have a baby elephant in the barn."

Then the Little Old Woman said, " But I do want him to have a roof over his head. I must get busy and see what I can do."
56

The Little Old Woman got some lumber from her cellar. She found a hammer and a saw. Then she went to work.

Bang! Bang! went her hammer. Soon a shed was ready. The Little Old Woman put some hay in it and called to the baby elephant.

The baby elephant walked right into the shed! Then the Little Old Woman put some lumber across the front of it.

Now the baby elephant could not get out. When he walked away, his shed went with him. Bump! Bump! Bump!

"What a funny baby elephant!" said the Little Old Woman. "He likes to take his shed around with him."

The little shed went bump, bump, all over the garden. Down came the bean poles! Down came the tall corn!

"My, oh my!" said the Little Old Woman. "This will never do. I must use my head and think of something."

So the Little Old Woman went into her little old house. She sat down in her little old chair. She used her head and she used her head. Before long, she thought of something to do.
58

"I will put wheels on the shed," said the Little Old Woman. "That is what I will do. Then the baby elephant can roll his little shed around with him."

So the Little Old Woman put four wheels under the elephant's shed. Now the baby elephant was happy again.

When the goose and the duck went to the pond nearby, the baby elephant rolled right along with them.

He blew water over the goose and the duck. He blew water over the top of his shed. What fun the baby elephant had!

59

The Little Old Woman sat down under her cherry tree. All at once she heard a noise.

Down the country road many wagons were coming. Men were shouting as the big horses trotted along.

" Listen ! " said the Little Old Woman. " That must be a circus ! It is on the way to the next town."

The baby elephant heard the noise, too. He watched the clowns and the monkey cages go by. He heard the lions roar.

Soon the baby elephant saw the big elephants coming. How glad he was !

He stopped eating and away he ran. He ran all the way to the road.

Then the baby elephant walked down the road with the big elephants. His little shed rolled right along with him.

The Little Old Woman watched him go.

"My!" said the Little Old Woman. "The baby elephant must have been with the circus. I never thought of that!"

Then the Little Old Woman called, "Good-by, Baby Elephant! I shall miss you very much."

The Little Old Woman sat down and watched the circus go on down the long country road.

"I like baby elephants," she said. "I'm so glad this baby elephant will always have a roof over his head! And that's because I used my head!"

The Elephants

With their trunks the elephants
Hold hands in a long row—
Their little eyes so quick and wise,
Their feet so big and slow.
They climb on top of things and then,
When they are told, climb down again.

Dorothy Aldis

All Around the City

63

Ben and the Ball Game

Ben came running into the apartment. "Mother! Mother!" he called. "Guess where I'm going."

Ben's mother tried and tried to guess, but she could not.

"Father is going to take me to a ball game," said Ben. "A big ball game!"

"A game at the ball park!" said Mother. "That's good news! I'm glad you can go."

"Yes," said Ben. "We are going on Saturday! Next Saturday!"

The days went by. Ben thought that Saturday would never come.

Then one morning Ben said, " Today is Saturday, Mother. This is the day I'm going to the big game ! "

Ben put on his new baseball suit. Then he got out his baseball glove.

" I'm ready for the big ball game now, Father," said Ben.

" But Ben," said Father. " You are not going to play ball. You are going to see a ball game."

" I know," said Ben. " But I think I will take my glove with me, Father."

65

Soon it was time to go to the game.

"Ben," said Mother. "You are not going to play baseball at the park. Must you take your baseball glove with you to the game?"

"Please, Mother! May I?" asked Ben.

Mother laughed. "Take it if you wish, and have a good time," she said.

Away Ben and Father went to the ball park. They soon found their places and sat down.

Ben looked all around. He had never seen so many people. Wherever he looked, there were people all around him.

Then the game started. Ben had never seen a game like this! Sometimes the people around Ben jumped up and shouted.

Whenever Father got up, Ben got up. Whenever Father shouted, Ben shouted. What fun Ben had!

66

Ben was happy as he sat there and watched the game. He had one hand inside his big baseball glove all the time.

The game went on. Ben thought first one side would win and then the other.

All at once there was the loud pop of a ball. Everyone watched the ball go high into the air. Up, up, up it went!

All the heads in the city ball park turned. All the people looked at the ball high in the air.

67

Ben watched the ball, too. High into the air it went! Then the ball began to come down.

Down, down the ball came. It was coming right at Ben.

Ben jumped up. Up went his hand in the baseball glove.

Then thump went the ball! It was a loud thump! And there was the ball right in Ben's glove!

How everyone laughed! How they shouted! The people all around Ben called, "Good catch, boy! Good catch!"

All the people at the game were talking and laughing. Ben's father was talking and laughing as loud as anyone.

Ben looked up at his father. He looked at the ball in his baseball glove. Then Ben said, "I did play ball. Didn't I, Father? Didn't I?"

Father laughed. "Yes, you did," he said. "It is a good thing you had your glove. You did play in the big game after all!"

Two Horses

It was Saturday. Ben and Mary Ann were going to Spring Street Park to ride on their bicycles. They liked to go to the park to play.

" May we take Joe to the park with us today ? " asked Mary Ann.

" Yes, Mother," said Ben. " Joe wants to ride his new stick horse in the park."

"All right, Ben," said Mother. " This is a good warm day. Joe may go with you. Take care of your little brother."

Then away the children went to Spring Street Park.

70

Ben and Mary Ann took their bicycles. Joe took Trot, his new stick horse.

Trot was a funny little stick horse. He had a head just like a horse, but he rolled along the ground on two wheels.

Round and round the park went Ben and Mary Ann on their bicycles. Round and round went Joe on Trot.

Trot could go fast—as fast as little brother Joe could run. But Trot could not go as fast as the bicycles.

" Let's race to the big gate," said Ben.

" Come this way, Joe," called Mary Ann. "Follow us to the gate. It is not far."

Joe tried to keep up with Ben and Mary Ann. Soon Joe was far behind. He began to go faster.

" I think they went this way," he said. " Get up, Trot! Get up!"

Joe rode Trot up a little hill on his way to the gate. Then down the other side of the hill he went.

Joe rode Trot up and down another little hill. Trot! Trot! Trot! How his little stick horse did roll over the ground!

Still little brother Joe did not see Ben and Mary Ann. Where could they be? He stopped and looked all around to see if he could find them.

Joe did not see Ben and Mary Ann. He did not see the big park gate. But he did see a big brown horse coming along. A man was on the horse.

72

The man on the brown horse was big. He was dressed in a blue suit. Joe saw that the man was a policeman.

"Please, Mr. Policeman," called Joe. "I want to find Ben and Mary Ann. I want to go to the big park gate."

"That's a long way for a boy to go on a stick horse," said the big policeman. "Would you like to ride to the gate on my horse?"

Joe was so happy he could not talk. His head went up and down, and up and down again.

73

The policeman put Joe and Trot on the big brown horse. Then he jumped up and sat behind them.

Joe had never been on a real horse before. Once he gave the horse a little pat just because he was so happy.

" Hold on now," said the policeman. " Hold on ! " And away they went.

Soon Joe and the policeman rode up to the big park gate. There were Ben and Mary Ann.

" Joe ! Joe ! " called Mary Ann. " We have been looking for you ! "

" Where have you been, Joe ? " said Ben.

" I have been for a ride," said Joe. " On two horses ! And one of them is real ! "

74

Dolly

Dolly is an old horse
With a white star.
She's a great deal nicer
Than young horses are.

She always takes sugar
Gently from my hand,
And she's perfectly willing
Just to stand.

She doesn't stamp and kick
When I use the currycomb,
And always when I think we're lost
She knows the way home.

Elizabeth Coatsworth

Red Roofs, Green Roofs

There were rows and rows of little white houses on a new street in a big city.

Each little house looked very much like the one next to it. But some of the houses had red roofs and some had green roofs.

Jack and his mother and father had just moved to the big city. They lived in one of the little houses that had a red roof.

76

Jack liked to live in the little white house with the pretty red roof. He liked to see the postman who came by each day.

One day Jack did not wait to see the postman. He was going to the store to get some groceries for his mother.

"You know your way to the store, Jack," said Mother. "Can you find your way home? We have just moved here, you know."

"Oh, yes," said Jack. "I know this little house with the red roof."

Jack walked down E Street past the little white houses. He went around the corner past the baker's shop and the bus stop. Then he came to the store.

Jack was glad to see Mr. Mulligan who worked in the big store.

Soon Jack had the groceries his mother wanted. Butter and bread were in the bag. There was fruit for breakfast, too.

"Good-by, Mr. Mulligan," called Jack. "I must hurry home with the groceries."

Jack went back past the bus stop and the baker's shop. He looked at the sign on the corner.

"E Street," said Jack. "This is my street. Now I can find my way home."

78

Jack walked down E Street. There
were so many houses! And each one
looked like all the others!

Jack stopped at one white house with
a red roof, but it was not his. There
was a yellow seesaw near the front walk.

Jack stopped at another house. A
green sprinkler was watering the grass
in that yard.

At another house he saw a bowl of
goldfish in the big front window.

" We do not have any goldfish at our
house," said Jack. So on he went.

The ice cream man saw Jack stop and look around. " Is something the matter, little boy ? " asked the ice cream man.

" I cannot find my house," said Jack. "All the houses look the same on E Street."

Just then Jack saw his mother in a yard down the street. " I see my house ! " said Jack. " My mother is in the yard." Away he ran to his own home.

Each day after that Jack played on the grass in his front yard. Each day Jack saw the ice cream man come down E Street. But he did not buy ice cream.

" I will keep my money," said Jack. And back into his pocket the money went. Then one day Jack took out all of his money and counted it.

" I have enough money now," Jack said to his mother.
80

"Enough money for what?" asked Mother as she came out of the house.

"Guess!" said Jack. "It will be something to make our house different from all the others on the street."

"Let me think about it," said Mother. "Something to make our house different!"

"Yes, we can get it at Mr. Mulligan's store!" said Jack.

"I'm going to Mr. Mulligan's store now," said Mother. "Come along with me."

Soon Mother and Jack came to the big store. Jack stopped outside. He stopped beside a box of flowering plants.

"Flowers!" said Mother. "Big red flowers will make our little white house different from all the others!"

Before long Jack's house did look different.

When Jack walked down E Street now, he still went past rows and rows of houses. He still saw the bright yellow seesaw and the water sprinkler in the yards.

But Jack knew his house now. He knew that the house with the bright red flowers in the yard was his own.

82

Oscar and the Bus Driver

Oscar was a little squirrel. His home was in a big tree in Spring Street Park.

Right under Oscar's tree was a big round sign that said, " Bus Stop."

At first Oscar did not like the buses that stopped under the tree. He would run behind the tree and peep out at them.

That was how Oscar first met his friend, the bus driver.

One day when Oscar was peeping out at the bus driver, a wonderful smell came his way.

The driver had stopped the big bus and was eating peanuts. Oscar watched. He smelled and smelled. He did not move.

The bus driver looked up and saw Oscar. " Have a peanut ! " he said. Then he threw a peanut down by the tree.

Oscar waited until the bus was gone. Then he ate the peanut. He liked it.

The next time the bus driver came to the bus stop, he called to Oscar.

" Here, Oscar," he called. " Here is another peanut for you."

That is how Oscar got his name and that is how he got a new friend.

84

Soon the squirrel and the bus driver were good friends. The driver always threw down a peanut for Oscar to nibble when the bus stopped.

One day the driver put a peanut on the bus step. Then he called, "Come and get it, Oscar."

Oscar looked at the peanut. He wanted it, so he jumped up on the step. Then quick as a flash, he climbed back up the tree with the peanut.

After that Oscar watched for his good friend, the bus driver, every day.

Oscar soon learned to take peanuts from the driver's hand.

One day Oscar jumped right up on the step of the bus when it stopped. He sat there and waited for a peanut.

The driver put his hand in his pocket. But when he brought his hand out, it was empty.

" No peanuts ! " said the bus driver. " Jump down, Oscar. Scat ! I will bring some peanuts the next time I come."

Oscar did not jump off the step. He just sat and waited for a peanut.

The people at the bus stop waited, too. They wanted to get on the bus, but Oscar did not move.

The driver called to the people who were waiting. " Has anyone here brought some peanuts along ? " he asked.

Pockets were turned inside out. But there were no peanuts. Not one!

" Listen, Oscar," said the bus driver. " I must go. Jump down now. The very next time I come, I'll bring you a bag of peanuts."

Oscar did not move. He sat on the bus step and waited.

Just then a little boy called, "I have a peanut." It was Bob Baker who was waiting with his aunt.

Bob came up to the bus step with the peanut in his hand. He opened his hand, and Oscar took the peanut.

Then down the steps Oscar ran. Quick as a flash he was up in the big tree where he nibbled the peanut.

The people laughed as they got on the bus. They were all glad that Bob had a peanut for Oscar.

"I'll never come to this bus stop again without some peanuts for Oscar," said the bus driver. And he never did.

The Little Farm in the Big City

Abel and His Neighbors

Abel lived in a little house in a big city. Behind the house was a little yard.

On one side of the yard was a high building. On the other side of the yard was another high building.

Mr. Gates lived in the high building on one side. Aunt Susan lived in the high building on the other. If Abel made much noise, they told him to stop.

Mrs. Hall had a high fence at the back of the yard. If Abel threw a ball at the fence, Mrs. Hall told him to stop.

89

It was Saturday. Abel looked around the little back yard.

"Yes, it will do," he thought. Abel went into the cellar and brought out a shovel from the furnace room.

"Some of the other children in school have gardens," thought Abel. "I will have one, too." He picked up the cans and sticks and stones. Then he took the shovel and began to dig.

Mr. Gates heard the noise and looked out of his window. He was surprised when he saw what Abel was doing.

"Good morning," he said. "I see that your farm is about ready to plant."

"Farm?" asked Abel.

90

"Yes, but you cannot have a farm without corn. But I suppose corn will not grow in the city." Then Mr. Gates put his head back inside the window.

"Farm?" thought Abel. "Farm? A farm would be something like a garden— but much better. I will plant some corn."

Abel had some money. So he went to the corner store. Soon he came home with a little bag of corn.

Abel looked around the yard with the corn in his hand. Abel knew how to plant beans, but not corn!

Just then a window opened. It was Mr. Gates again. "Abel, is that corn?" called Mr. Gates.

"Yes," said Abel. "It is. I wish I knew how to plant it."

Mr. Gates knew how to plant corn. So he told Abel just what to do.

"Put four seeds in each hill," said Mr. Gates. "I suppose you have heard the old rhyme?

> One for the squirrel,
> One for the crow,
> One for the chicks,
> And one to grow."

Soon Abel had planted the last seed in the very last hill. Then he looked up to see if Mr. Gates were watching.

But all Mr. Gates said was, "Whoever heard of growing corn in a big city?"

92

Mr. Gates' rhyme could not have been right. The squirrels and the chicks and the crow did not get this corn.

Soon four little green plants were growing in each hill. Abel tried to count the plants in all the hills, but there were too many to count.

One day when he was working in his corn, Aunt Susan looked out of her window. "Good morning, Abel," she said. "Is that a farm in your back yard?"

"Yes," said Abel.

Aunt Susan said, "It will not be a real farm without cabbages. But I suppose cabbages will not grow in a city." And down went her window.

93

Abel still had some money left, so he went to the corner store to get some cabbage plants for his farm.

Aunt Susan must have been watching from her window, for she called out, "Are you planting cabbage?"

"Yes, purple cabbage," said Abel.

"Purple cabbage!" said Aunt Susan. "Maybe I can tell you how to plant purple cabbage." So she did.

Abel wanted to have a real farm. So he planted the cabbage the way Aunt Susan told him.

Then Abel looked up at her window.

All Aunt Susan said was, "Whoever heard of growing purple cabbage in a big city?"

94

Mrs. Hall looked over the high fence. "Well! Well! Well!" she said. "Are you planting a farm, Abel?"

"Yes, I am," said Abel.

"If it is a real farm, you must have squash," said Mrs. Hall. "But whoever heard of planting squash in a big city?" Then she went in her back door.

Abel had just enough money left to buy squash seeds. He went all the way to the corner store to get some.

When he came back, Mrs. Hall was looking over the fence again.

She told Abel how to make little hills and how to plant the seeds. "Just a little way under the ground!" she said.

A Surprise for Abel

The corn, the cabbage, and the squash were up now. How they did grow!

One day it rained and rained. Mr. Gates looked out of his window and saw the puddles in the rows of corn.

" That rain will be good for your farm, Abel," called Mr. Gates.

On other days the sun was bright. It made the ground good and warm.

Aunt Susan would call out of her window, " You cannot have too much sun. As long as we get rain too, it will be all right."

Mrs. Hall would call over the fence, " What a good farm this is going to be ! "

96

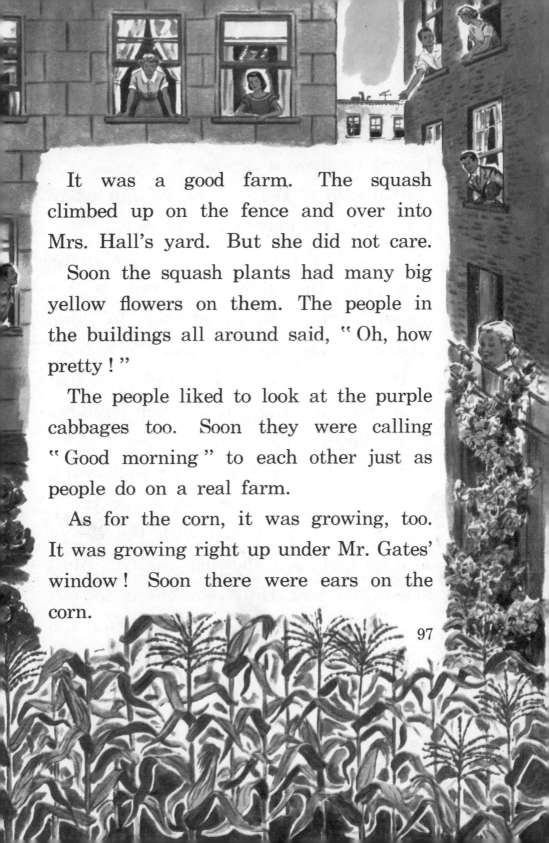

It was a good farm. The squash climbed up on the fence and over into Mrs. Hall's yard. But she did not care.

Soon the squash plants had many big yellow flowers on them. The people in the buildings all around said, " Oh, how pretty ! "

The people liked to look at the purple cabbages too. Soon they were calling " Good morning " to each other just as people do on a real farm.

As for the corn, it was growing, too. It was growing right up under Mr. Gates' window ! Soon there were ears on the corn.

97

" I think this is very good corn ! " said Mr. Gates. " May I have this ear, Abel ? I want to show it around."

Abel said, " Yes." Then he ran off to play ball. He played a long time.

When Abel came home, he saw many people in the street in front of his house. They all called out to him, " How are you, Farmer Abel ? "

Abel knew many of the people. He had seen them looking out of their windows at his farm.

When Abel went into the back yard, someone shouted, " Here is Farmer Abel."

There was Mr. Gates with the ear of corn he had been showing around. Aunt Susan and Mrs. Hall were there, too !

One man took Abel's picture for the newspaper. Another asked him how he had learned to farm.

98

Then Abel saw two men who were talking into a radio mike.

"Let me tell you, people, it is about the best corn I ever saw," said one of the men by the radio mike.

"There are cabbages and squash that would win a prize anywhere," said the other man. "They are as pretty as a picture."

99

"Now, here is Farmer Abel," said the first man with the radio mike. "Come and tell us what you are going to do with the money you earn on your farm."

Abel said, "I'm going to buy more seeds and a sprinkler with the money I earn. I want a new baseball glove too."

The man by the radio mike talked again. "Thank you, Farmer Abel," he said. "I think that you have earned a baseball glove!"

Then he said, "Good-by, radio friends. That's all for today. That's the story of the little farm in the big city."

100

Up and Away

Airplane Andy

Flying with Father

Andy liked airplanes. His home was not far from an airfield. So he could watch the airplanes come and go.

Andy was always talking about airplanes. He liked to make pictures of airplanes too. That is why everyone called him Airplane Andy.

Andy's father was a pilot, and Andy wanted to be a pilot someday, too. He wanted to be a good pilot like his father.

One day Andy's father was ready for a trip. He was flying in a small airplane to a new airfield not far away. Father told Andy that he could come along, too. Andy was very happy.

As they came to the airfield, they saw the little airplane on the runway. It was all warmed up and ready to go.

Father and Andy got in and took off. Zoom! Zoo-om! Up and away they went.

Then the little airplane flew straight ahead. The engine of the airplane made a noise that Andy liked to hear.

On they went. Andy looked out at the mountains. He looked down at the towns and fields as they flew along.

"How would you like to take the stick
with me, Andy?" asked Father. "Put
your hand here. Pull back when you want
to go up. It takes just a little to make
her go up or down."

What fun Andy had! He wished this
trip would be a long, long one.

They came to the new airfield all too
soon for Andy. Then down, down they
went. Andy and Father got out of the
little airplane.

104

Andy's father went about his work.

Andy had a good time talking with the pilots. He liked to watch the men who took care of the airplanes too.

He watched the airplanes come and go. Some stopped for gasoline and then went on their way. Others were made ready for long trips.

Andy watched the travelers come and go. He looked with care at all the new airplanes. He wanted to make pictures of them when he got home.

The day went by too fast for Andy. Soon he and his father started for home.

105

The Trip Home

At first Andy and his father flew fast and straight ahead. All at once the sky began to grow dark.

"I see a storm coming," said Father. "We will fly around it."

Bump! Bump! went the little airplane. Up and down, up and down it went.

Andy could see the dark sky in front of them. He could hear the loud roar of the storm.

"Can we make it, Father?" asked Andy.

"Yes, Andy," said Father. "We shall soon fly around this storm."

Andy was not afraid. He knew that his father was a good pilot. He knew that he had been in many storms.

Andy sat back. He watched his father
as they flew on and on.

Then all at once something splashed
on Andy's shoe. It was oil.

At the same time he heard his father
talking. "Andy, something is the matter
with the oil," said Father.

" I see a leak," called Andy. " There
is oil on my shoe. The oil is leaking ! "

Andy's father had to think fast. He
could not leave his place to take care of
the oil leak.

"Andy," said his father. "You can help me. Look in the pocket beside you. Find the roll of tape there. I will tell you how to tape the leak."

Andy did as he was told. He rolled the tape around and around the pipe.

"Good work," said Father. "Now hold your hand around the tape on the pipe. Stay with it, Andy. Hold on!"

Andy's hand was around the pipe. He did not let go. He was holding on as his father had told him to do.

"Stay with it, Andy," said Father. "We shall soon be there. I can see the lights at the airfield now!"

"No oil is leaking from the pipe," said Andy. "But I will not let go."

Then down, down went the airplane. It rolled across the field and stopped.

At last Andy could take his hand away from the pipe. How glad he was!

"Good boy, Andy!" said Father. "The tape is put on just right. You will make a good pilot some day."

Andy was happy. That was what he wanted to be—a pilot—and a good one like his father.

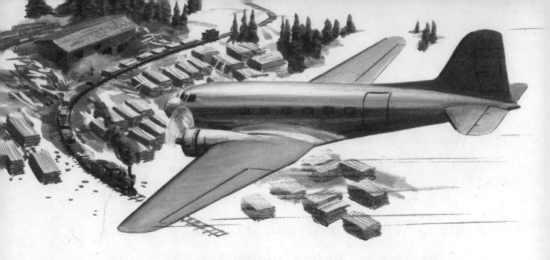

The Flying Firemen

Up and up flew the big airplane. Away from the airfield it went with a roar.

"Just the same old trip," said the pilot. He looked down out of the window.

"There is the same train we always see on the track here," said the pilot. "And the same little red caboose."

"There is the same lumber mill," said the co-pilot. "And the piles and piles of lumber by the loading station."

"I like flying over mountains and farms better," said the pilot. "We shall soon be in the country."

The co-pilot liked flying over farming country best, too. He liked to look down on the green and brown fields.

The pilot had been flying this same trip for a long time. He knew all of the big farms along the way. He looked down now at one of the farms.

"It looks as if our farmer is going to plant wheat this time," he said. "He is doing good work with that tractor."

The co-pilot said, "Look! What is that by the farmhouse? It looks like smoke. Turn back and fly low!"

"Yes, it looks like a fire!" said the pilot. "I can see the smoke now."

R-r-r-roar! went the airplane as it turned and flew back over the farmhouse. The plane flew low and straight ahead. Then back over the big farm it went. R-r-r-roar! R-r-r-roar! R-r-r-roar!

Soon the plane flew over the smoke by the farmhouse.

"I see the fire now!" said the pilot. "It is the barn. The roof is on fire. It must have just started to burn."

"I don't see a fire engine," said the co-pilot. "I don't think the farmer knows that his barn is burning."

"We must let them know that something is the matter," said the pilot. "If the barn burns, so will the house."

Around the airplane went once again. Roar-r-r-roar, it went! The pilot could see the smoke coming from the barn roof.

R-r-r-roar! went the plane. Low over the roof of the house it flew. It made so much noise that the dishes rattled on the table in the farmhouse.

The pilot turned the plane around and brought it back over the house again.

112

Now the pilot could see the farmer's wife in the yard. She had heard the noise. Now she knew why the airplane had been flying so low over her house. She saw that the barn was burning.

The farmer's wife waved something white in the air. She wanted to say thank you to the pilot.

"She sees the smoke now," said the co-pilot. "Let's watch and see what happens next."

Soon the pilot saw two big fire engines come up the road. Four or five cars were right behind them.

113

"I guess the farmer's wife must have telephoned for the fire engines in a hurry," said the pilot.

Then away went the airplane. The pilot took one look back at the fire. He could see just a little smoke now.

The big airplane climbed high into the sky. Zoom! Zoom! Soon the plane had left the farm far behind.

"I suppose they will call us 'flying firemen' after this," said the co-pilot.

That is just what happened. Now the farmer and his wife watch for the big airplane every day. When it flies over the farm they say, "There go the flying firemen."

114

Peter and the Pilot

It was about dark when Peter came out of the big red barn.

He climbed up on the barnyard fence and sat looking out across the fields to the dark mountains.

There was much work to do on a ranch. There were cows to milk and sheep and lambs to care for. But now the day's work was over.

Flip, Peter's dog, came to the fence. He wanted Peter to come into the ranch house. He knew it was time to eat.

115

Peter did not go into the house. He sat on the fence and waited. He threw a little stick up in the air and watched Flip run to get it.

Then he put his hand into his coat pocket and took out his big flashlight.

The wind was blowing and it was growing cold. Peter buttoned up his coat. He knew it would be dark soon.

" I guess the plane is not coming tonight," said Peter. " It is after seven."

Just then Peter heard a noise overhead. It was not the wind. It was the loud roar of an airplane engine.

Each night at about this time the big plane came over. Its engine roared high in the air over the ranch house.

Peter watched for the plane every night. He did not like to go into the ranch house until it came over.

116

Peter listened. Tonight the sound of the engine was different. It was very different. And the plane was flying far too low.

"Something is the matter!" said Peter. "The plane never flies this low." Peter jumped down from the fence.

Just then the sound of the engine stopped. Peter listened. The engine started again. It made a loud roar and then it stopped again.

"Something is the matter with the engine," thought Peter. "It may be out of gasoline. The plane may have to come down. But where? How can I help?"

All at once Peter thought of something he could do. He pulled his flashlight out of his pocket. Then he flashed it up into the air three times as he ran across the yard.

Peter ran with his flashlight to the flat field behind the barn.

" This is the best place around here for a plane to land," thought Peter. "And this field may be too small."

Again and again Peter flashed the light across the flat ground. Then he flashed the light up into the air.

Would the pilot see the light?

Just then the lights on the plane
flashed off and then on again.

" The pilot sees me all right," said Peter.
He flashed the light across the field
again.

Down, down came the plane. Its roar
made Peter's ears roar too. Then the
plane landed on the corner of the field.
It bumped straight across the field
and stopped.

Peter ran across the field. As he
came up, he saw a man crawling out of
the plane.

"Wow!" said the pilot. "Something
is the matter with my engine. Thank
you for helping me make a landing."

Peter's mother heard the airplane land and saw the lights in the flat field. She came out and asked the pilot to have supper with Peter.

The pilot telephoned the airfield for help. Then he and Peter had pancakes and honey for supper.

Peter said, "I sit on the fence and watch for you every night."

"I will flash my lights to you after this," said the pilot. "You are a real friend, Peter."

"I will flash back with my flashlight," said Peter. "Maybe I will be a pilot when I grow up, if I'm not too busy being a cowboy!"

120

Big Fellow and the Airfield

Pat rode along on his bicycle. He was so happy, he sang as he rode. He was on his way to see his best friend.

Pat's friend was not a boy, a dog, or a pony. This friend was a giant shovel. His name was Big Fellow.

Pat's father had helped to make Big Fellow. One day he let Pat come into the shop to see the big shovel being made.

Pat liked Big Fellow so much that he went back to see him again and again.

One day Father said, "In three more days Big Fellow will start his first job. He is going to help build the big new airfield."

Pat was happy. Think! Just think! His great friend Big Fellow was to help build the new airfield.

Now at last the big day was here! "Suppose something happens to Big Fellow," Pat thought. "Suppose his engine will not work. Suppose his wheels do not go round. Suppose Big Fellow breaks down!"

Pat could not get to the airfield fast enough. Soon he saw Big Fellow standing in the flat field. He was ready for his first big job!

Some men were working nearby. They were about ready to start Big Fellow. Big Fellow would soon start to work.

122

Three of the workmen near Big Fellow were talking. "This is going to be a big job," said one.

"This will be one of the best airfields in the country," said another. "It will have all the new ways to help planes land."

"It will have long, long runways," said the other workman. "This will be a good place for big planes to land. But there is much work to be done before the airfield is ready."

Pat was watching Big Fellow. This was a big job. Could Big Fellow move the great stones and the sand? Could he do this big job?

Pat waited for the engine of the giant shovel to start.

Then Put-r-r-r! went Big Fellow. Put! Put-r-r-r-r!

Pat watched. Yes! Big Fellow was doing his job. Clinkety-clank he went. Clinkety-clank!

Pat was so happy he wanted to shout. His friend Big Fellow could move the stones and sand. Good for Big Fellow!

124

Big Fellow did not break down. He worked for days on the new airfield. Other big shovels worked, too.

At last the long, long runways were ready. The great new airfield was done. Now many airplanes came to the busy airfield every day.

Many travelers rode in the big planes that went from city to city.

Some of the airplanes took letters to faraway places.

Hm-m-m! went the engines of the big airplanes. And away they flew!

Yes, Big Fellow had done a good job!

Hoppy, the Helicopter

Hoppy, the helicopter, looked down at the landing field.

" This must be the place," he thought. Then down he went. Straight down to the landing field !

Hoppy saw many different airplanes on the landing field. There were big long airplanes. There were small bright airplanes.

But Hoppy could not see any other helicopters. So he looked again.

126

" Who are you ? " called one of the long airplanes.

" I am a helicopter," said Hoppy. " This airfield is my new home."

" I am a jet plane," said the long airplane. " I make fast trips to faraway places. Have you ever done that ? "

Before Hoppy could say anything, another long plane roared, " I take travelers to faraway places. Have you ever done that ? "

" You look like a little bug," said the jet plane. "Are you some kind of bug ? "

Hoppy didn't like to be called a bug. He did not know what to say or do. He wished that he could go and hide.

127

Hoppy did not like this landing field. For days and days he just sat in a corner and waited. Nothing happened.

Then one morning Hoppy heard many loud sounds and much talking.

Someone was calling, "A pilot is down in the mountains. Calling all planes! Calling all planes!"

"I can help now," thought Hoppy. "This is a job for me. A helicopter flies in and out of the mountains better than any other kind of plane."

Just then two silver jets roared down the runway one after the other. Up and away they went, up and away to the mountains!

Hoppy watched them go.

Soon the silver jets came back. "A jet flies too fast and too high," they said. "We cannot find the lost pilot."

128

One of the pilots at the airfield ran over to Hoppy in his corner.

"I will take the helicopter and look for the lost pilot," he said. "This is a good job for a helicopter."

Other men at the airfield came with gasoline and oil. Soon Hoppy took off!

Straight up Hoppy went. Then he started to fly to the mountains.

Hoppy flew all around the sides of the mountains. In and out of the canyons he went.

"We must hurry," thought Hoppy. "Soon it will be too dark to see down into the canyons."

129

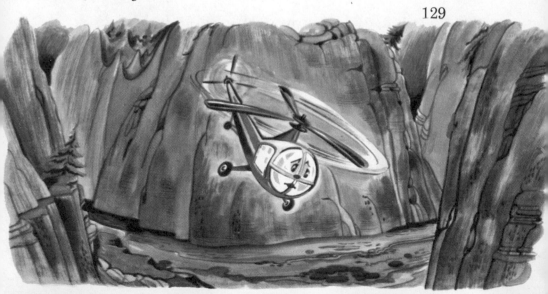

All at once Hoppy saw something move
in one of the canyons. He saw that it
was a man waving his hands and shouting.

The pilot and the co-pilot saw the man
in the canyon, too. So the pilot let
Hoppy drop down, down. Straight down!

"The ladder!" called the pilot to the
co-pilot. "Let down the rope ladder."

Hoppy stopped right over the lost
pilot. Down went the ladder. Soon the
lost pilot had the rope ladder in his
hands. Then he started climbing up.

130

Up and up and up climbed the lost pilot. Soon he was in the helicopter.

Straight up out of the canyon, and off to the airfield Hoppy went.

As he landed at the airfield, Hoppy heard a great roar.

The jets and all the other airplanes were calling to Hoppy. They were all roaring together.

"Good for you, Hoppy!" they roared. "We need a helicopter at this airfield. We are glad you have come to make your home here. We need you."

131

Something to Think About

When airplanes get as thick as cars,
And people ride from earth to Mars,
Will traffic lights be made of stars?

Carolyn Forsyth

132

Once Upon a Time

133

The Boy and the Door

There was a small shop on a little street in an old city. In the shop were beautiful things made of silver and gold.

The small shop had a door that opened on the little street. A shopkeeper was standing at the open door.

"Come and buy! Come and buy!" called the shopkeeper. "Come into my shop and see all the beautiful things!"

Again he called, "Come in! I will show you beautiful things made of silk. I will show you beautiful things made of silver and gold!"

134

One day the shopkeeper had to go on a trip to the king's castle. The king wanted a beautiful silk coat and a silver cup from the shop.

The shopkeeper called to the boy who worked for him. "I am going to the king's castle," he said. "You must stay here. Do not leave the door of the shop."

As the shopkeeper left, he turned around and called again to the boy. "Do not leave the door of the shop whatever happens," he said. "Do you understand?"

"Yes, I understand," said the boy.

The shopkeeper walked through the open door to the street where his horse and wagon waited.

The horse pulled the wagon along the streets of the old city. Soon he went through the big gates and up to the door of the castle.

The shopkeeper gave the king the silk coat and the silver cup. Then he went on his way.

Before long, the shopkeeper was back at the shop of beautiful things. He stopped and looked up in surprise.

"What is this?" he cried. "Why are so many people going into my shop?"

Then the shopkeeper saw that the door of the shop was gone and so was the boy who worked for him.

136

Just then the shopkeeper saw the boy.
He was standing on the street near the
shop. The boy had the shop door out in
the street with him. He was watching
some men who were doing tricks.

The shopkeeper ran to the boy. "I
told you not to leave my shop," he cried.

"No," said the boy. "You told me not
to leave the door. I did just as you said.
I did not leave the door. I have the door
here with me."

Jack and the Beanstalk

The Wonderful Beans

Jack's mother looked in the empty storehouse in the cellar.

" There is nothing in the house to eat, and we have no money," she said to Jack. " You must take our cow to town tomorrow and sell her."

The next morning Jack tied a rope to the cow and started out to sell her. He had not gone far when he met a little man. The little man had a bag of beans in his hand.

" Boy, do you want to sell that cow ? " asked the little man.

138

"Yes, we must sell our cow," said Jack. "I'm on my way to town to sell her."

"I will give you some wonderful beans for your cow," said the little man. Then he opened his hand and showed Jack the beans. They were red and blue and yellow.

Jack looked at the beans. They were the most beautiful beans that he had ever seen. The more Jack looked, the more he wanted them.

"Here is my cow," said Jack. "I'll take the beans. Then I'll run home and show them to my mother."

But when Jack gave his mother the beans, she threw them out of the window.

"Jack! Jack!" she cried. "Now our cow is gone. Our money is gone. And we have no food. What shall we do?"

The next morning Jack sat up in bed and looked around. The room looked dark. He jumped out of bed and ran to the window. There he saw a tall, tall beanstalk.

The beautiful beans had come up in the night. Jack ran into the yard. He could not see the top of the beanstalk.

"How tall is it?" he thought. "I'll climb to the top and see." So up and up Jack climbed. Then he climbed and climbed some more.

At last Jack came to the top of the beanstalk ladder. There he saw a big stone castle.

Jack supposed a king lived there. The long climb had made Jack hungry. So he went to the castle to ask for food.

140

Inside the Castle

A tall woman with a kind face opened the castle door.

" Come in," she said. " But watch out for the giant. He might come home. He might come at any time now. You must not let him see you. The giant does not like little boys ! "

Before Jack could eat his supper, he heard loud footsteps on the stairs. Thump ! Thump ! Thump ! The giant was coming home.

" Here he comes ! " called the woman. " Quick ! Run and hide behind the door."

The giant sat down at the big long table to eat his supper. Jack peeped out at him through a hole in the door.

Soon the hungry giant had gobbled up all the food on the table. He ate a sheep, three lambs, a goat, two dishes of soup, and seven apples.

Then he said to his wife, "Bring me my pet hen! Be quick now!"

The giant's wife brought the hen and put her on the long table.

"Hen, lay an egg!" shouted the giant.

At once there was an egg of gold on the table.

142

"Now lay another," said the giant. Then there was another egg of gold on the table.

When Jack saw the wonderful hen, he knew that she had been his father's hen.

Jack's mother had told him about this wonderful hen. She told him that a giant took the hen from their family. Now here was that same hen!

Jack watched the giant through the hole in the door. Jack saw him playing with the eggs of gold. Everything was still. Soon the giant went to sleep.

Jack crawled out from behind the door. He took the hen and ran down the beanstalk to his home.

Jack's mother was happy to see the hen again. Soon they had many eggs of gold. Now they could sell the eggs and buy all the food they wanted.

The Giant's Treasures

The next day Jack climbed up to the giant's castle again. He thought that he might get his father's money bags.

" Come in," said the tall woman. " But be quick and hide. The giant is coming."

Jack heard the giant's loud steps on the stairs. Thump! Thump! Thump! Jack ran to hide in the chimney corner.

The giant ate his supper. Tonight he ate a cow and many, many pancakes. Each pancake was as big as a wagon wheel.

Soon the giant called for his five money bags. He opened the bags and counted his treasure of silver and gold. Before long he went to sleep.

Jack came from the chimney corner. He took the money bags and ran down the beanstalk. Soon he was home again.

144

Days went by. Then Jack said, "I think I'll go up the beanstalk tomorrow. I might find my father's harp."

"It was a great treasure," said his mother. "But watch out for the giant!"

Again Jack climbed up the beanstalk. Again he went to the giant's house. And again the tall woman let him in.

Soon Jack heard the giant's footsteps on the stairs. Thump! Thump! Jack ran to hide behind the big black stove.

The giant ate his supper. Then he called for his harp. Now this wonderful harp could play and sing. Soon it played and sang the giant to sleep.

Jack crawled out from behind the big black stove and took the harp. He ran out of the castle with it.

145

As soon as Jack started to run, the wonderful harp began to tinkle and sing.

The giant heard the harp and ran after Jack. Jack went down the beanstalk and the giant started down after him.

Jack was little and could run fast. Soon he was down to the ground. "Mother," he called. "Quick! Come and help me cut down the beanstalk."

Jack and his mother cut the beanstalk and down fell the giant. Thump! Thump! When the giant fell, he made a great hole in the ground. Down, down he went into the hole.

Jack and his mother took the harp into the little house. Now they owned the hen, the money bags, and the harp again.

Many times Jack's mother would say, "They were wonderful beans. Now we shall never be hungry again!"

146

Mr. Rabbit, Rain-maker

We Need Rain

The animals were all talking together.

" Rain ! When will it rain ? " they said.

" I want rain on my field of wheat," said Mr. Wolf. " The ground is very dry."

" The brook is dry, too," called the crow from a tree nearby.

" We must have rain on our corn," said the squirrels.

" What shall we do ? " said the robin.

Mr. Rabbit did not say anything. He did not like to farm. He had one cabbage in his back yard. Sometimes he would throw a little water on it.

147

One day Mr. Fox and Mr. Bear came to Mr. Rabbit's house. They sat near the doorway and talked and talked.

They were still talking about the rain they wanted.

Mr. Rabbit just sat there. He did not say anything.

At last Mr. Bear said, " How is your garden this summer, Mr. Rabbit ? "

" My garden is pretty good," said Mr. Rabbit. " It could be better. But it is pretty good for a summer garden."

148

Mr. Bear looked at Mr. Fox. Then Mr. Bear said, " Have you had any rain at your house, Mr. Rabbit ? "

" I guess it is not what you might call a rain," said Mr. Rabbit. "A little water here and a little water there."

Mr. Fox and Mr. Bear were surprised to hear this. " How can you get rain when we cannot get a drop ? " they asked. " What is the secret ? "

" Well," said Mr. Rabbit. " Some of my neighbors do call me a rain-maker. They may be right. Then again they may not be right. They can call me whatever they please."

Mr. Bear and Mr. Fox went away. They soon told all the other animals about Mr. Rabbit's secret.

" He can make it rain," they said. " We will ask him to make it rain for us."

149

Soon the animals came to Mr. Rabbit's house. There were so many of them that they were all over the yard.

Mr. Wolf was doing most of the talking. "Please, Mr. Rabbit," he said. "Make it rain. Please help us out."

" Yes, yes," said all the others.

" Well," said Mr. Rabbit. " First you must pay me. A rain-maker must have his pay. Are you ready to pay ? "

All the animals ran to their homes. Soon they came back. Mr. Wolf brought wheat. The squirrels brought nuts and corn. Mr. Bear brought flour and butter.

Some animals brought one thing and some brought another. Flour, corn, wheat, nuts, and fruit ! Each one brought something to pay Mr. Rabbit, the rain-maker.

150

How Much Rain?

"I see that you want it to rain," said Mr. Rabbit. "Now the next thing is to find out how much rain you want."

All the animals began to chatter at once. They all wanted to tell Mr. Rabbit how much rain they wanted.

"Wait!" said Mr. Rabbit. "This is too much noise for me. Just go down beside the river and talk this thing over."

As they started off Mr. Rabbit called to them, "Come back and tell me how much rain you want."

151

Mr. Rabbit took all the food and put it in his cellar. Then he said, " I'll go over by the river and see how things are coming along. I'll hide in the tall grass and listen."

So that is what he did. And what Mr. Rabbit heard made him laugh. The animals were still talking about how much rain they wanted.

Mr. Wolf wanted a big rain. Mr. Ring Tail, the raccoon, wanted a little rain.

Mr. Frog and Mr. Turtle called for much rain. Tiny Mr. Field Mouse lived in the ground and wanted very little rain.

152

All the birds had something to say, too. The owl and the crow wanted just a little rain. But the robin wanted enough to make puddles to splash in.

The animals by the river talked on and on. They talked until the sun went down. Some wanted one thing and some wanted another.

Mr. Rabbit, the rain-maker, sat in the grass and said nothing at all. At last all the animals went home. Mr. Rabbit went home, too.

How Mr. Rabbit laughed! His trick had worked. He had all the food that he wanted. And he did not have to make it rain at all!

"Just as I thought!" laughed Mr. Rabbit. "Just as I thought!"

The Rabbit

Brown bunny sits inside his burrow
Till everything is still,
Then out he slips along the furrow,
Or up the grassy hill.

He nibbles all about the bushes
Or sits to wash his face—
But at a sound he stamps and rushes
At a surprising pace—

You see some little streaks and flashes—
A last sharp twink of white
As down his hidy-hole he dashes—
And disappears from sight.

E. L. M. King

154

Tom Thumb

Tom and the Cow

Once there was a tiny, tiny boy named Tom Thumb. He was about as big as his father's thumb. Tom had a tiny coat and a wee little hat.

One day Tom's mother dressed him in his tiny coat and his wee little hat. Then she took him with her when she went to milk the cow.

The cow was in a field near the barn. Tom's mother put him on top of a big thistle. Then she began to milk the cow.

The tall thistle plants around Tom were blowing in the wind. Soon Tom's wee little hat blew away.

155

"Mother, Mother," called Tom. "The wind blew my hat away. It may blow me away too!" His mother stopped milking the cow. She tied Tom Thumb to one of the tall thistle plants.

"Now, hold fast," she said. Then she went on with the milking. Tom did hold fast. He tried not to be afraid.

The thistle where Tom sat was not far from the cow's head. Soon the cow began to reach for some of the thistles that were around Tom.

All at once the cow reached out for the very thistle where Tom sat. Into the cow's mouth Tom went with the thistle.

Tom was afraid. He called out, but his mother did not hear him. Then Tom shouted, "Help, Mother, help!"

"Where are you, Tom? Where are you?" cried his mother.

"I am in the cow's mouth, Mother," shouted Tom. "Please help me, Mother! Help me!"

Tom's mother began to cry. She did not know what to do.

"Help me, Mother!" Tom cried again.

The cow was surprised at all the noise. She opened her mouth, and out Tom jumped.

Tom's mother was glad to see him. She put him in her pocket and ran to the house. When she found that Tom was all right, she was so happy that she cried.

Tom's mother got him some clean clothes. Then she gave him a tiny, tiny cup of milk before he went to bed.

Tom and the Old Horse

Tom liked to ride in the cart pulled by the big farm horse. So he went to the field with his father every day.

One day at sundown Tom said, " Father, I want to help. Please let me take the horse and cart back to the barn for you."

Tom's father laughed. " You are such a tiny boy," he said. " You are too tiny to be the driver of such a big horse."

" Oh no," said Tom. " I will sit in the horse's ear. Then I can call out the way the horse is to go."

The horse was old and lazy and did not go very fast. So Tom's father let the boy have his way.

" Let's see if you are a good driver," said Tom's father. He picked Tom up and put him in the horse's left ear.

158

"Get up," called Tom. But the lazy old horse did not start.

Tom's father gave the horse a quick pat on the back. Then the horse started across the field with Tom in his ear.

When Tom came to the gate he said, "Go left." The lazy old horse did not understand what Tom said. But he turned left because that was the way to the barn.

Tom wanted to go faster. "Trot fast," called Tom. Still the horse did not understand. But he wanted his supper of corn and hay, so he started to trot.

Tom was so pleased that he began to laugh and shout.

159

Tom's mother was out in the barn. She was surprised when she saw the horse and cart come through the barn door.

" Where is my good man ? " she cried. "And where is Tom Thumb ? "

" Here I am, Mother," called Tom. " Here I am. Take me down, please."

" Where ? " asked his mother. " Where are you, Tom Thumb ? "

" In the horse's ear," called Tom. " I am the driver. I brought the horse and cart home for Father. Please take me down now, Mother."

His mother was pleased that Tom Thumb was learning to help his father. She took him down and gave him a big drop of honey for his supper.

160

Out of Doors

Bushy Tail

" The children are coming," said Mother Chipmunk to Father Chipmunk. " I can hear them. Here they are now ! "

Up through the round hole by the old tree came four little chipmunks. Their father and mother watched them.

How fine the baby chipmunks looked in their coats of brown ! Each one was holding his tail up over his back.

Three of the little chipmunks stayed at home. They did just what their mother told them to do.

But not the frisky little chipmunk named Bushy Tail ! Something was always happening to Bushy Tail.

162

"Come on," said Bushy Tail to the other little chipmunks. "I know where the field mouse lives down by the brook. Come with me and I will show you."

"No, Bushy Tail," Mother Chipmunk called to him. "You must not go away from your home."

"You are not old enough to go as far as the brook," said Father Chipmunk. "You must not go far away from our doorway. What if a big fox comes?"

"Father and I must go into the woods now," said Mother Chipmunk. "We must find something for breakfast. Stay here and play while we are gone."

The little chipmunks watched their father and mother go into the woods.

163

Then Bushy Tail said to the others,
"Let's go and see the field mouse for a
little while."

"No, Bushy Tail," said the good
little chipmunks. "We must not go to
see the field mouse. Mother wants us to
play near our doorway."

The four little chipmunks jumped over
the stones on the old wall. They rolled
in the grass and leaves. They ran
around the roots of the old tree.

Then all at once there were just three
little chipmunks playing by the old tree.
Bushy Tail was not there!

"Mother! Father!" called the three
little chipmunks. "Come home. Come
home. Bushy Tail is lost!"

Mother and Father came running back through the woods. Bushy Tail was lost! So many things could happen to a little chipmunk who did not watch out! And Bushy Tail did not watch out for himself!

" Where did you see him last ? " called Mother Chipmunk.

" He was right here," one of the little chipmunks told her. " We were running around the big tree. Then all at once Bushy Tail was not here any more."

" He is gone," said another little chipmunk. " We cannot find him. Where is he, Mother ? "

" Bushy Tail ! Bushy Tail ! " called Mother Chipmunk. But Bushy Tail did not come.

165

Mother Chipmunk was very sad. Bushy Tail was gone. She did not know where to look for him.

Just then a little chipmunk called to her from the doorway. It was Bushy Tail himself! " Here I am, Mother," he said. " Do not look sad. I was not lost at all."

Mother Chipmunk ran to Bushy Tail. " Where have you been ? " she said. " What happened to you ? Tell me about it, Bushy Tail."

"A very strange thing happened to me, Mother," said Bushy Tail. " You will be surprised when I tell you about it."

" Go on," said his mother. " Tell us about the strange thing that happened."

" We were playing," said Bushy Tail. " I was looking for a place to hide. I ran behind the flat stone near the roots of the old tree."

166

"Yes," said Mother Chipmunk. "Then what happened?"

"I saw a pile of dry leaves there," said Bushy Tail. "So I ran under the leaves to hide."

Then Bushy Tail said, "I saw a little round hole under the pile of leaves. So I went down into it."

"Did you go down, down, down ever so far?" asked his mother.

"Yes," said Bushy Tail. "I went down, down, and then I fell into a big room. Where do you think I was, Mother? I think I must have found a new way into our house."

167

"No," said his mother. "It is not a new way. You found our secret doorway. Your father and I made the secret doorway when we came here to live."

"Every chipmunk home has its own secret doorway," said Father Chipmunk. "Someday our family might need to get out of the hole in a hurry."

"Come with me now," said Mother Chipmunk. "I will show all of you how to use the secret doorway that Bushy Tail found."

168

Across the River

"We must swim across the river," said Father Beaver. "The big fire in the woods has burned all the trees around our old home."

"Yes," said Mother Beaver. "We must swim across the river and build a new home. See how green the trees and grass are over there."

"Follow me," said Father Beaver. So Mother Beaver and the brown baby beavers followed him to the side of the river.

169

"We are ready," said Father Beaver. "I will not swim fast. Stay as near to me as you can." Then he jumped into the water.

The little beavers liked to swim. They liked to splash the water with their flat tails.

They had never tried to swim across the river before. But the baby beavers knew they must go with their father.

One by one the beavers followed their father into the water. Their mother watched them go.

170

"Look, Mother! See me catch the others," called Splash. He was the last one to go. As he jumped into the water a stone rolled over on his foot.

Mother Beaver ran to help him. But Splash was gone before she could reach him. "My foot is all right, Mother," he called. "Come on."

Mother Beaver watched Splash swim along by himself after the others. Then she started across the river, too.

The little beavers had fun. This was a long swim, but they liked it. On they went across the river.

171

Soon Splash fell behind the others.

"Mother!" he cried. "Mother!"

Mother Beaver heard the cry. She knew that something was the matter with her baby's foot.

"I'm coming," called his mother. And there she was by his side.

"Do not be afraid," she said. "I will swim under you. Then you can get on my back. I will take you across the river."

Down into the water went Mother Beaver. When she came up, Splash was on her back!

Splash was not afraid now. He lay very still on his mother's back until they were across the river.

Mother and Father Beaver were happy. All the family had come across the river. Now they could build a fine new home.

172

Mother Blacktail and Her Twins

Mother Blacktail was standing by the big tree. She looked all around. She listened. She did not want anything to happen to her twins.

Mother Deer was about ready to leave now. She was going through the woods to the brook. Before she left, she stopped to see that the twins were all right.

One twin lay at the roots of a tree near an old log. The other twin lay on the soft dry grass and leaves nearby.

Mother Blacktail was a good mother. She knew just how to take care of her twins in the woods.

Soon after Mother Blacktail left, a cottontail rabbit came through the woods. Hoppity-hop! Hoppity-hop he went!

He came right by the big tree and ran through the grass. He did not see the deer twins near the log.

Hoppity-hop! Hoppity-hop! Over the log he jumped. Then down he came right on the back of one of the twins. Thump!

What a surprise for the baby deer! And for Bunny, too! He bounced high into the air and ran away as quick as a flash.

Mother Blacktail was drinking at the brook not far away. She heard the noise and stopped drinking. Then she came running back through the woods.

Soon the mother deer was beside the twins. How glad they were to see her!

174

But Mother Blacktail did not stay with her twins very long. Again she heard something. It was a dog barking and running through the woods.

Mother Blacktail listened. Was the dog coming down the hill? Was he following the brook? Would he find the baby deer?

"Bow-wow! Bow-wow!" said the dog. The sound of the dog's barking came nearer and nearer.

The mother deer knew just what to do. She waited until the dog saw her. Then off through the woods she ran.

At first Mother Blacktail did not run fast. She wanted the dog to follow her. She did not want him to find the twins!

In a little while she ran faster. The dog ran faster, too. Soon they were far away from the little deer twins!

Mother Blacktail knew the woods and fields very well. She jumped over logs. She ran like the wind. She was on her way to the high hill.

The hill had many stones on it. The dog could not run very fast there.

But Mother Blacktail jumped over the stones and ran fast up the hill. Soon she was far away from the dog! Her trick had worked!

Then Mother Blacktail started back to her twins by the old tree. They were sleeping when she got there. They knew their mother would take care of them!

176

Little Pond in the Big Woods

Far away in the big woods was a little pond. The animals thought the little pond was beautiful. And it was.

An old log reached out over the water. A black bear sometimes walked along the log. He came to the pond to catch fish.

Rabbits nibbled the soft green grass that grew near the big log.

A mother duck quacked to her baby ducks near the shore. Bees buzzed around the flowers that grew on the shore nearby.

The birds and the raccoons liked the little pond, too. Just at dark the deer came to the pond for a drink of water.

177

One summer it was very hot for many, many days. There was no rain at all, and the hot sun was drying up the little pond.

The grass that the rabbit liked to eat turned brown and dry. There were no flowers for the bees to buzz around. There were no fish for the black bear to catch with his paws.

Still it was very hot, and still no rain came. One day the deer came for a drink. There was not one drop of water left in the little pond.

178

"What shall we do?" asked the deer. A wee brown bird in a tree called, "Yes, what shall we do?"

All the other animals said the very same thing, "What shall we do?"

From the other side of the tree came a loud quack.

"I know!" quacked the duck. "Far away through the trees, there is a big blue lake. It is so big that the sun cannot dry it up. I saw it as I flew over the woods."

All the animals were listening to what the duck said.

"Will you go to this big lake?" said the duck. "I will show you the way."

"We will go," said the animals. "We must have water!"

179

"Quack! Quack!" called the duck. "Just follow me!"

"We are coming," thumped the rabbit. And he started over the dry brown grass.

All the other animals followed, too. Through the hot dry woods they went.

The raccoons joined them along the way. At the top of the hill they met the big black bear. "I'll go too," he said.

The deer called to a butterfly, "Come on. We are going to find water. You may ride on my back."

"Come on!" called the brown bird from a treetop. "I see the lake far ahead."

On they went. It was a long, long way. The woods were dry and it was very, very hot. But on and on they went.

180

All at once there was a loud noise overhead. It was the duck. She was flying back over the treetops.

"I have found it! I have found the blue lake," quacked the duck. "There is water enough for all."

The animals stopped to listen to the good news.

"I saw green grass and flowers there," quacked the duck. "It is not far now. Come this way!" Once again the duck flew on ahead.

On they went. Nearer and nearer they came. Soon they could see the blue water of the big lake.

181

Water! Water! Water! How good it was. How pretty it was. And how wet! For many, many days the animals stayed by the big blue lake.

There was water to swim in and water to drink. There was green grass and there were many beautiful flowers.

But the animals still missed their own little pond in the woods. This big lake was not their real home.

One day the sky was gray, and big, big raindrops started to fall. The rain splashed on the big blue lake.

Soon the grass and flowers were wet and so were the trees. All the animals were glad to see the raindrops fall. The birds were glad, too.

182

Then one morning the sky was blue again. The sun came out and the rain was over.

From high over the trees the duck flew down to the big lake. "The rain has brought water to our little pond," she quacked. "I have been there. We can go back home now."

The deer and the bear heard. So did all the others. They were happy, for they liked their little pond best of all!

"Let's go now," said the deer.

"I'm ready," buzzed the bee.

"Quick! Come on!" called the raccoons.

"One more swim," said the frog. "Then I'll be ready, too."

Off they started. The duck went ahead and showed the others the way.

The bear followed the bee. Next came the deer with the butterfly on his back. The rabbit and the raccoons followed the deer. Last of all came the little frog.

Back through the woods they went. The woods were pretty now and the grass was green. The animals did not think the trip a long one this time.

Soon the animals came to their pond. How happy they were to get back home!

The little pond was happy, too. It was glad to see all its old friends, each and every one of them!

184

Johnny and Teeny

Two little bear cubs, Johnny and Teeny, were waiting near the gate in the big park.

Many other bears were waiting near the gate, too. All of them were hungry.

Every day at sundown a small truck came through the gate. It brought cans of leftover food from the picnic places in the park.

The bears were waiting for the truck to come. Teeny and Johnny were playing while they waited.

185

Teeny climbed into an empty red can and sat down. He looked like a toy bear sticking out of a Christmas surprise box.

Soon Johnny bumped the red can. It rolled along until it turned over. Then Teeny fell out.

The big bears watched the cubs at their play. But when the big bears heard the truck coming, they turned and ran to the salad bowl.

The salad bowl was a big hole in the ground. It was the place where the truck driver always put the leftover food.

The driver threw the leftover food from the big cans into the salad bowl. Then he went away.

The big bears began at once to turn the food over with their noses. How good it did smell to them! And how they did eat!

186

Teeny and Johnny ran to the salad bowl, too. But the cubs could not get their noses near the food. There was no room around the salad bowl for them.

"Gr-r-r-r!" said Teeny as he tried to get to the food. But the big bears would not make room for the little bear.

Teeny and Johnny smelled the food. They were hungry, too. So they started looking for a place to eat.

A row of empty cans was standing near the salad bowl. The little cubs had to run around the cans to get to the food.

Then bump! The two little cubs ran right into the row of big empty cans.

187

Bang! Over went one of the big empty cans. When it fell over, it rolled with a bang right into the next can.

Then all the cans in the row went down one after another. Rattle-bang they went! Rattle, rattle! Bang, bang!

The big bears around the salad bowl had never heard such a noise. They did not wait to see what had happened. They left what they were eating and ran into the park woods.

Soon there were no big bears at all near the salad bowl. So Johnny and Teeny had a good supper that night. A very good supper for two hungry little bear cubs!

188

Stories for Fun

The Seven Little Piffles

One day the wind blew and blew. It blew the hats right off the heads of the seven little Piffles. It blew the hats off the gardener and the baker, too.

The big wind took Mr. Piffle's hat right over the bus station.

" Such a wind ! " said Mr. Piffle. " Our hats are gone and we shall never, never get them back ! "

" Well, they were old hats," said Mrs. Piffle. " We can get some new hats now."

190

By the time night came, the wind had stopped blowing. The next day was bright and beautiful.

" What a fine Saturday this is ! " said one of the little Piffles. " May we go on a trip to the canyon, Mother ? "

" Yes," said Mrs. Piffle. " You may go to the canyon. But stay together and please come home in time for dinner."

Off went the seven little Piffles. Up hill and down hill they walked. Soon they came to a small canyon.

"Look! Look!" called Peter Piffle.
"Just look in the canyon!"

The seven little Piffles looked. They saw something that made their mouths pop open in surprise.

There in the canyon in front of them were piles and piles of hats.

There were hats of all colors. Red hats! Green hats! Pink hats! Purple hats! Black hats! White hats!

There were hats of all kinds too. Girls' hats! Boys' hats! Hats with feathers! Hats without feathers!

192

Mrs. Piffle went to the window when dinner was ready. She wanted to see if the seven little Piffles were coming. What a surprise she got!

The little Piffles were coming up the street. They were loaded down with all kinds of hats.

"We found our hats," called the little Piffles. "The wind blew them right over the big hill and into the canyon."

"We found the gardener's hat," said Patsy Piffle. "And all these hats too."

"My! Oh my!" said Mrs. Piffle. "What shall we do with all these hats?"

Ebenezer Piffle looked at the piles of hats. " I know what to do," he said.

" What ? " shouted all the other little Piffles.

" I will show you," said Ebenezer. " Bring the hats and come along with me."

The little Piffles followed Ebenezer. Soon they reached the city park. They put all the hats on the grass by the picket fence.

" Now do as I do," said Ebenezer. He picked up some hats and walked along beside the picket fence. Then he put a hat on each picket.

The other little Piffles ran to help Ebenezer put the hats on the pickets.

What a strange-looking fence it turned out to be ! The people all laughed when they saw so many different hats on the picket fence.

194

" Step right up and get your hats ! "
called the seven little Piffles. And
that is just what people did.

" There is my tall silk hat," called
Robin Turner.

" I see my little hat with all the dots
on it," said Patsy King.

The gardener and the fireman came.
The baker came in his little blue cart !
All the people came to get their hats
off the picket fence. By night all the hats
were back on the right heads.

It was a good day for the seven little
Piffles. They laughed and laughed as they
ran all the way home.

The Wonderful Washing Machine

"Come with me, Ann," said Mother. "We will take the clothes in here to be washed. Then we will go next door for the groceries. We need some bread, a can of soup, and some milk."

"May I wait for you here by the washing machines?" asked Ann. "I like to see them work."

"All right," said Mother. "I will be back soon. You may sit here by the washing machines and wait for me."

Ann sat down in a chair in front of the busy machines.

196

The washing machines had little windows in front. Ann could see the wet clothes going around and around in the water. Splashing, rolling, splashing!

Around and around went the wet clothes. Bzrrr, bzrrr went the washing machines!

" They sound like airplanes," thought Ann. " Such funny . . . funny . . . airplanes . . ." Soon she went to sleep.

Then Ann began to dream. She dreamed that one of the washing machines was an airplane, and she was in it. She was flying over a big white farmhouse in the country.

Ann dreamed that two children were in the back yard. They were helping their mother with a basket of wet clothes.

" We must hurry," said the children's mother. " I have a mountain of clothes to wash before we can go on the picnic."

197

Ann landed her plane in the yard of the farmhouse.

"I can help you," she said. "This machine flies like an airplane, but it washes clothes, too. It is a wonderful washing machine."

The two children ran to see the wonderful washing machine.

"Bring your clothes!" called Ann. "We will get them washed in no time."

The children helped throw the clothes into the wonderful washing machine. Then bzrrr, bzrrr, went the wonderful washing machine! Bzrrr, bzrrr!

198

Just then someone called to Ann. It was her own mother back from the store next door.

"Are you ready to go, Ann?" said her mother. "I have all the groceries now. Is the washing ready?"

Ann looked up in surprise. Her dream was over! "Yes, Mother," she said. "I think the washing is ready."

Ann was still thinking about her dream. She was still thinking about the fun that she had on her trip in the wonderful washing machine.

"Oh, Mother," said Ann. "There is a wonderful washing machine here. I will tell you all about it on the way home."

199

Timothy, the Little Brown Bear

Every morning all the animal children in the woods went to school. That is, they all went but Timothy Bear.

" I do not want to learn to read," said Timothy. " I can find honey in the woods without learning to read. I will just have fun."

So all the other animal children went to school without Timothy.

" I think I will go and ask Uncle Rabbit to tell me some stories," said Timothy. He walked through the woods until he came to Uncle Rabbit's house.

I will be back soon. Please sit down and wait.

There was a sign on Uncle Rabbit's door. As Timothy could not read, he did not know what the sign said.

Timothy called and called. But Uncle Rabbit did not come to the door.

"I guess Uncle Rabbit is out visiting," said Timothy. So he went away.

Soon Timothy met Uncle Rabbit. "I went to see you," said Timothy. "But you were out visiting."

"Why didn't you sit down and wait?" said Uncle Rabbit. "Didn't you read the sign on the door? The sign said, 'I will be back soon. Please sit down and wait.'"

201

The next day Timothy took a bowl of honey and went to visit old Mr. Owl.

"We will eat bread and honey," thought Timothy. "We can talk and have a fine time together."

Timothy walked through the woods to the tree where Mr. Owl lived.

Mr. Owl had put a green chair by the door. There was a sign on the chair.

"Oh, I know all about signs now," said Timothy. "They say, 'I will be back soon. Please sit down and wait.'"

So Timothy sat down in the chair to wait. But he soon jumped up. He was covered with wet paint. He had paint on his suit, and paint on his paws and face.

"Help, this is wet paint!" said Timothy.

Just then Mr. Owl put his feathered head out of his front door.

"Oh, Timothy! Timothy!" he called. "You are all covered with paint. Why didn't you read the sign? The sign says, 'Wet Paint.'"

Then Mr. Owl said, "Why don't you learn to read, Timothy? Why don't you go to school with Mac Mouse and the robin twins?"

"I don't want to go to school," said Timothy. "I don't want to learn to read."

Timothy tried to clean off the wet paint before going home to his mother.

203

After breakfast the next morning,
Timothy went out to play. He saw
something sticking out of his mailbox as
he went by.

"I know about signs now," said
Timothy. "That paper says, 'Wet Paint.'
Someone has painted our mailbox. I will
stay far away from it today."

So Timothy did not go near the
mailbox. He just sat under a tree in
the back yard all by himself.

Inside the house Timothy could hear
his mother stirring up a ginger cake.
She stirred and stirred the ginger cake.

Soon Billy and Betty Bunny came down the road. Hoppity-hop! Hoppity-hop! They had a big bowl of cabbage salad with them.

Along came the five squirrel brothers with an apple pie and a basket of nuts.

By and by the chipmunk boys came along with a big fruit pie. Behind them came the robin twins and the mouse family. Each one had a covered basket.

Last of all came Toddle, the turtle. Toddle had a pan of candy on his back.

"Where are they all going today?" thought Timothy. "It looks like a picnic to me." So he followed the others down the road to the old mill pond.

205

Timothy soon found the animals. They
were on the grass that grew by the old
mill pond. He peeped around a big tree.

Yes, it was a picnic! It was the most
wonderful picnic that he had ever seen!
Timothy was so sad he began to cry.

"Why are you crying?" called Toddle,
the turtle. "Why don't you come to the
picnic?"

"Because I was not asked," cried
Timothy. "You didn't want me to come
to your picnic."

"But we did want you to come," said
Mac Mouse. "I saw the postman put the
letter about the picnic in your mailbox."

206

"A letter?" said Timothy. "I thought that was a sign that said, 'Wet Paint.' So I didn't go near the mailbox."

Then Timothy saw Mother Bear coming with the ginger cake and his letter. He stopped crying and started to laugh.

"Now you can see that it is always good to know how to read," said Mother Bear.

The very next day Timothy went to school with the other animal children. Before long he could read as well as anyone in the woods.

Mrs. Goose and the Strange People

The Animaltown people were coming back from their picnic in the woods. Mrs. Hen looked up at the bright stars.

" Do you suppose there are people living on the stars ? " asked Mrs. Hen.

Old Mrs. Owl said, " There may be people on the stars. But if we saw them, they would look strange to us. I have read about them in one of my books."

Most of the animals laughed at old Mrs. Owl. But not Mrs. Goose. She thought about the strange people on the stars all the way home.

The next morning Mrs. Goose was working in her kitchen. She made two big cherry pies. She washed her pink dress with the purple dots on it.

All at once Mrs. Goose heard something. Outside her door, there were strange soft footsteps. Nearer and nearer they came.

Soon Mrs. Goose heard the footsteps right in the next room. Tip, tip, tip!

Mrs. Goose peeped around the door. She saw three strange little people.

One of the strange little people had on a tall shiny hat. Another had on a long sea-green dress. The other had on a hat with long ears sticking through it.

209

Mrs. Goose didn't wait to see anything
else. She knew just what had happened.

This was the very thing they had
talked about last night. Here were some
of the strange people from the stars!

"Help! Help!" called Mrs. Goose. And
she raced out of her front door to Mrs.
Squirrel's house across the street.

"Come and help me, Mrs. Squirrel,"
called Mrs. Goose. "The strange people
from the stars have come. They are in
my house right now. They will break
everything I have."

210

Mrs. Squirrel and Mrs. Hen were talking in the kitchen.

"Did you make up this story, Mrs. Goose?" asked Mrs. Squirrel.

"No! No!" cried Mrs. Goose. "Three of the strange people are in my house right now."

Mrs. Goose ran down the street to Mrs. Rabbit's house.

"Mrs. Rabbit!" called Mrs. Goose. "Three strange little people from the stars are here in Animaltown! One has a shiny hat. One has a sea-green ..."

"Oh, Mrs. Goose," said Mrs. Rabbit. "The strange little people you saw are my three little rabbits."

Mrs. Rabbit began to laugh. "They dressed up in funny old clothes," she said. "They wanted to surprise you. Where are my children, Mrs. Goose?"

"They are in my house," said Mrs. Goose. "You can come and get them right now!"

Mrs. Goose and Mrs. Rabbit went into Mrs. Goose's house.

They looked in the front room. They looked in the kitchen. They looked all over the house. But the rabbit children were not there.

212

"Where are my children?" cried Mrs. Rabbit. "Please come and help me find them, Mrs. Goose."

Mrs. Rabbit ran out of the kitchen door. Mrs. Goose followed her.

They went up and down the streets. But they could not find the rabbit children. So they went back to Mrs. Rabbit's house.

"I want to get my coat," said Mrs. Rabbit. "Then we will look some more."

Mrs. Goose sat down on a big chair to wait. All at once Mrs. Goose said, "I think I hear a noise. There is someone else in this house."

Mrs. Rabbit and Mrs. Goose looked in the bedroom. There were the three rabbit children in their own little beds.

"Well! This is strange," said Mrs. Rabbit. "My children never go to sleep in the daytime without being told."

"It is a strange day if you ask me," said Mrs. Goose as she started home.

Mrs. Goose ate one of her cherry pies when she got home. Then she took the other pie to the three little rabbits. How they ate that cherry pie!

Mrs. Goose laughed. "These little people like cherry pie," she said. "So they are not so strange after all."

214

In City and Country

The Best Surprise

"What's all this?" asked Father as he came into the apartment. "Where did you children get all the big red hats?"

"Mother made them," said Mary Ann. "The hats are for the Spring Street Singers. We are going to sing over Station WMQ today. Betty is going to sing with us."

The children were laughing and talking as they tried on the big red hats. All but Betty! She did not laugh. She did not talk much.

216

Betty did not live in the city. She was visiting Mary Ann. Betty's home was on a ranch and she was thinking about the ranch now. She looked a little sad.

"I wish my mother could see me in this big red hat," she thought.

"I will take you to Station WMQ now if you are ready," called Father.

"Come on, Betty," said Mary Ann. So Betty put on her big red hat.

Father wanted to make Betty laugh. He sang a funny little jingle.

> "Betty, Betty
> In the big red hat,
> You look pretty
> And that is that."

The children all laughed as they started out for Station WMQ with Father.

WMQ was in a tall building downtown. The children followed Father into the elevator on the first floor.

They went up and up to a room at the top of the tall building. A sign on one of the doors said,

> **The Children's Own**
> **Saturday Morning Show**

Just then a woman in a gray suit opened the door. She saw the children.

"Are you the Spring Street Singers?" she asked. "Come right in. We shall be ready for you in a little while."

Soon a tall man came into the room. He was the announcer. When a red light flashed on, he began to talk.

The announcer said, "And now the Spring Street Singers will sing for you. They are Mary Ann, Susan, Patsy, and Betty."

The announcer looked at the children. "These children have never been on TV before," he said. "We heard about them and asked them to sing today."

The children sang one song. Then they sang another and another. It was fun!

Next the announcer said, "Thank you, Spring Street Singers. Do you suppose your mothers are watching you today?"

Then Betty began to talk. And how she did talk! "My mother is in the country," she said. "We live on a ranch. I am visiting friends in the city."

"How do you like the city, Betty?" asked the announcer.

"Oh, I like it very much," said Betty. "I like the park and the high buildings and the big stores and the bus rides."

Then Betty said, "But the city is not like our ranch. We have many cows and sheep and baby lambs on our ranch. We play in the hay and ride in the wagons. It is fun to live on a ranch."

The other children looked at Betty in surprise. They had never heard her talk so much before.

220

Betty was ready to go on talking. But the announcer said, "Thank you, Betty, and thank you, Spring Street Singers. Our time is up now. Good-by!"

The red light went off. The Children's Own Saturday Morning Show was over.

Just then the woman in the gray suit said, "Come this way, Betty. There is a telephone call for you."

Betty's face was bright and happy when she came back from the telephone.

"That was my mother!" said Betty. "She heard us sing and she saw me in my big red hat."

"Oh, Betty," said Patsy. "That was a good surprise for you."

"Yes, it was," said Betty. "I have had other good surprises in the city, too. But I think singing on TV is the best surprise of all!"

The Hollyberrys at the Shore

Jean was so happy she just had to sing!

" We are going to the shore,
We are going to the sea.
We are going to the shore,
We are going to the sea."

Everything was ready at last. The Hollyberrys were on their way to the seashore. They were going to stay there all summer.

There were sun hats, fishing poles, toy sailboats, and storybooks in the car.

Puppy was in the car, too. He sat on a big box of toys and looked out of the window as the car rolled along.

222

Soon they came to the seashore. Mr. Hollyberry stopped the car in front of a bright yellow house near the water.

"Here we are!" he said. "Let's all get ready for a swim now."

In no time at all the Hollyberrys were in the water.

Puppy thought he would go for a swim, too. But when he ran into the water, a great wave rolled him right over. He had water in his ears, in his nose, and in his mouth!

Puppy looked very surprised and very wet. He ran up and down and barked and barked at the water.

Another wave came along and rolled Puppy over again. So he soon learned that the sea was not at all afraid of his barking.

223

The children liked to dig and play in
the soft warm sand.

One day they made a big sand castle.
Jean made a wall around the castle. But
the waves soon washed the wall away.

Another day the children made pictures
in the sand. Then Jerry found a starfish.
Mrs. Hollyberry made a picture of the
starfish in the sand. It was fun to
play in the sand.

Then came the day that was the most
fun of all. That was the day when Mr.
Hollyberry helped make a big sand boat.

224

Jean and Jerry and Puppy got into the boat. "Here we go," shouted Jean. Then she made a rhyme about the boat.

"We are going for a sail,
We are sailing out to sea.
We are sailing in our boat,
As happy as can be!"

"We will sail away with you and look for treasure," said Mr. Hollyberry.

After a while Mrs. Hollyberry said, "Look! I see a sign sticking up in the sand over there."

Jean and Jerry jumped out of the sand boat and ran to the sign. It said,

225

Go to
the big stone

The children raced over to the big stone as fast as they could go. There they found another sign that said,

Dig here for treasure

"Treasure!" shouted Jean.

How she worked! Puppy and Jerry came and helped her dig. How the sand flew!

"Oh look! The treasure!" said Jean.

226

The children saw a big box with paper and rope around it. They took the box out of the hole and opened it.

In the box were many good things for a picnic lunch. There was cold turkey and bread and butter. There were apples and ginger cakes and nuts.

"This is a funny treasure," laughed Jean. "But it is a good picnic lunch. Who could have put it there?"

Mr. Hollyberry did not say anything. But Jean and Jerry could guess who put the picnic treasure in the sand.

227

The Little Woman Wanted Noise

Once there was a little old woman. She lived near a bus station in a busy city.

Street cars bumped past her door. Big trucks loaded with lumber rattled by. Gasoline trucks and street sprinklers went past. Cars and buses honked and honked their horns.

All day long people walked by the window. There were boys selling papers. There were children laughing and playing.

228

The little woman heard the merry sound of footsteps coming and going on her sidewalk all day long.

A shoemaker lived on one side of the little woman. All day long the busy shoemaker worked on shoes. He made merry shoemaker noises with his hammer and his machines.

On the other side of the shoemaker lived a man who made toys. All day long he made merry noises with his hammer and his saw. Bang! Bang! Ssss! Ssss!

Upstairs in the little woman's house lived a family with seven happy children. They laughed and they sang. Tra-la-la! Tra-la-la! Tra-la-la!

Up and down the stairs they ran all day with a thump, thump, thump.

Downstairs in the big cellar the old furnace went bang, bang, bang!

229

One day the little woman got a letter. It was from a friend in the country. It was a very short letter. It said,

> I am going to take a trip around the world. I will give you my farm. It is a good place to live.
>
> Your friend,
> Susan King

"That will be a good home for me," said the little woman. "I will sell my house in the city and go to the country."

So she did, and in a short time she moved out to the old farm.

230

The farm was a good farm. There were many green fields. There were fruit trees and a flower garden and a brook.

There was a little white farmhouse with a red roof and a stone chimney. The kitchen was clean and pretty, and the little woman liked it.

There was a big red barn too, but there were no animals in the barn.

The little woman missed the merry noises of the big city. She missed the bang, bang of the furnace. She missed the merry shoemaker noises.

She missed the thump, thump of the children going up the stairs too. It was very quiet on the farm.

231

The little woman sat in the chimney corner in her kitchen. She could not hear a sound. She did not like the farm because it was so quiet.

The little woman was sad. So she went to a neighbor's house and said, "What can I do to get some noise on my farm?"

"Buy some animals," said the neighbor. "Buy some animals that make noises. Buy a cow or a rooster. Who ever heard of a farm without animals?"

"Thank you," said the little woman. So she went away and bought a cow.

"Moo, moo," said the cow. The little woman thought that was a fine noise. But it was not enough. "I need some more noises on my farm," she said.

So the little woman bought a dog. "Bow-wow," barked the dog. The little woman thought that was a fine noise.

232

Now, all day long the little woman could hear "Bow-wow . . . moo, moo . . . bow-wow." She liked the noise, but it was not enough. So she bought a frisky cat and named it Scat.

"Mew, mew," said Scat, and the little woman thought that was a fine noise.

Now the noises on the farm went: "Mew, mew . . . bow-wow . . . moo, moo . . . mew, mew."

Still the little woman wanted more noise. So she bought a turkey.

"Gobble, gobble," said the turkey. The woman thought that was a fine noise.

233

Now the little woman had these noises: "Gobble, gobble . . . bow-wow . . . mew, mew . . . gobble, gobble . . . moo, moo." Still the farm was too quiet for her. So she bought a hen and a rooster.

"Cock-a-doodle-doo," crowed the rooster. "Cut, cut, cut, cut," said the hen. The little woman thought these were fine noises.

Then the hen sat on some eggs. Soon there were baby chicks on the farm. The little baby chicks ran all over the yard saying, "Peep, peep, peep, peep."

Now the little woman could hear many noises when she sat in her yard.

The noises went: "Peep, peep, peep . . . cock-a-doodle-doo . . . cut, cut, cut . . . gobble, gobble . . . mew, mew . . . bow-wow . . . moo, moo . . . peep, peep, peep . . . cock-a-doodle-doo."

The little woman liked all the noises, but still she wanted more. So she bought an old rattlety-bang car. The engine of the car steamed, and the horn made a loud honk.

So when it was too quiet the little woman sat in the rattlety-bang car. She honked and honked the loud horn.

Then the rooster and the other animals would all start up.

There would be a great noise like this: " Honk . . . peep, peep . . . gobble, gobble . . . cut, cut, cut . . . cock-a-doodle-doo . . . mew, mew . . . bow-wow . . . moo, moo . . . cock-a-doodle-doo . . . Honk ! "

But still this was not enough noise to please the little woman.

So one morning the little woman got into her rattlety-bang car and started for the big city.

She went up one street and down another. Then she came to a place where she heard more noise than she had ever heard before. The place was a school for boys who had no home.

The little woman stopped the old rattlety-bang car and listened.

The more she listened the more she liked the noise that she heard. So she got out of the old rattlety-bang car and went inside.

She saw big boys . . . little boys . . . tall boys . . . short boys . . . boys with black hair . . . boys with red hair.

What a noise all the boys did make! They were ringing bells, blowing horns, and shouting to one another.

236

"This is wonderful!" said the little woman. "How I would like to have some of these boys live with me!"

The little woman liked the big boy with the black hair. She liked the little boy with the red hair.

"They make more noise than any of the other boys," she said. "Just about five times more noise!"

So the little woman took the boy with the black hair home with her. She took his brother with the red hair, too.

After that, there was always noise on her farm. It was never quiet again.

Now the little woman was happy. She thought the country was the best place in all the world.

237

David's Silver Dollar

In the Fall

David had a shiny silver dollar. His father gave it to him on his birthday.

" You may buy anything you like with your dollar," said his father. " Buy something you want more than anything else in the world."

" Thank you, Father," said David. " I like this shiny silver dollar."

David made a wish as he blew out the candles on his birthday cake. He put the shiny silver dollar in his pocket.

238

David thought about the dollar for a long time, but he did not buy anything.

He didn't know what he wanted more than anything else in the world.

One day in the fall Mother was going downtown. David said, "Mother, may I go too? I want to go to the toy store."

"Yes, David," said Mother. "You can have your hair cut. Then we will have lunch." So David and Mother went downtown together.

David had just what he liked best for lunch. He had a bowl of turkey soup and some peanut butter on his bread. He had ice cream on apple pie, and milk to drink.

After lunch David and his mother went to the toy store. David put his hand in his pocket with the silver dollar. He was afraid the dollar might fall out before he was ready to spend it.

There were many things to see in the toy store. There were paints and paper and paste. But David had paints and paper and paste at home.

There were express wagons, sleds, and drums. There were toy cars and toy trucks. They were painted bright red and blue. Some had bells and some had horns.

"I have a toy car, and my friend Mac has a toy truck. I don't think I'll spend my dollar for a toy," said David.

So David did not spend his dollar in the fall.

240

Winter and Spring

Soon winter came. David and Mac put on their mittens and played in the snow.

They made a big snowman. They had fun throwing snowballs. They raced down the hills in the snow on their sleds.

When Christmas came, they had a big Christmas tree at school. They sang a Christmas song called " Jingle Bells."

One day that winter David went to a pet store. He saw goldfish and turtles and baby kittens. But David had a tiny turtle and Mac had goldfish.

David thought about his silver dollar many times that winter. But he did not know what he wanted most. So he did not spend his dollar in the winter.

David had a good time in the spring too. One fine spring morning he found a bright yellow basket by his bed. The basket had seven colored eggs in it.

The expressman brought him a white rabbit from Grandfather Turner's farm.

One day a man with a hand organ came by David's house. Tink-tink-tinkle went the hand organ! Tinkle-tinkle-tink!

May Day came. David wanted to get a May basket for his mother. "I can buy a basket of flowers for a dollar," he said.

But Mother said she liked flowers that grew in their own garden best. So David cut some flowers that grew in the garden and put them in a May basket for her.

That is why David did not spend his shiny silver dollar in the spring.

242

In the Summer

Then summer came. Mother and David went to the farm to see Grandmother and Grandfather Turner. Mother and David were going to stay in the country through the hot summer days.

David took his play clothes and his toys. He took his book of stories about Snipp, Snapp, and Snurr.

David showed Grandmother Turner the big shiny silver dollar in his pocket. "I don't know what I want more than anything else in the world," he told her.

Grandmother laughed. "Someday you will find just what you want. Then you will be glad that you have this shiny silver dollar. So hold on to it!"

243

David had fun on the farm. He played with the sheep and baby lambs. He played with the frisky little goats.

He rode with Grandfather on the hay wagon and on the big tractor. Clinkety-clank, clinkety-clank went the tractor all over the field.

David took his fishing pole to the brook to catch fish. He went with Uncle Joe when he took the big logs to the old sawmill.

David worked too. He helped build a garden fence to keep the cow out of the corn and beans. David was a very good gardener too.

Sometimes David played on the old organ in the corner of the living room.

Each day he ran to the mailbox by the roadside. He liked to get the mail when the country postman came by in his car.

244

One day David made a train in the
back yard. He made three cars out of
big egg boxes. Then he tied on a little
red caboose. David had a cowbell to
ring when he started the train.

Away went the cars. Away went the
little red caboose. " Get off the track ! "
called David. " Get off the track ! "

Uncle Joe came up from the barn. " I
am going to the store," he called. " Does
a boy named David want to go with me ?
A boy who will not break the eggs ? "

David jumped up. " I want to go," he
said. " And I will not break the eggs.
Please wait, Uncle Joe. I want to get
my dollar. I might want to spend it."

David in the Country Store

When they came to the town, Uncle Joe and David went to Mr. Fred's country store. David looked all around. There were many things to see in a country store!

He saw apples and eggs and butter. There were bags of flour and cans of soup and beans. There was paste and paper. There were buttons, paint, and rope.

David saw cowbells and dishes and candles. He saw kitchen pans and sun hats and sprinklers. So many things!

246

David sat down in one of the chairs by the big black stove to wait for Uncle Joe. Mr. Fred gave David a stick of candy to eat while he waited.

David thought about his dollar. But there was nothing in the store that he wanted more than anything else in the world. So he didn't spend his dollar.

On the way home Uncle Joe stopped beside a stone wall to talk to Mr. Zeke.

While the men were talking, David went into the back yard by himself to look around.

In the Neighbor's Yard

Under the sunflowers by the woodshed was a box. In the box were four little puppies. David sat down and looked and looked.

Then he put his hand in the box and took out one little puppy. It was black with a white face.

The puppy was soft and warm. Its tail was so short that it was not much of a tail at all. The little puppy had one white paw.

The mother dog came running to see who was looking at her puppies.

The mother dog saw that David was just playing with the little puppies. So she lay down beside David and thumped her tail on the ground.

David watched the puppies for a little while. Then he went around to the front of the house again. Uncle Joe was still talking to Mr. Zeke beside the stone wall.

"Would you sell me one of the little puppies?" David asked Mr. Zeke. "I can pay for it with my silver dollar. A puppy is what I want more than anything else in the world."

"Well, maybe you had better ask your mother first," said Mr. Zeke.

When they got home, Grandmother and Mother were under the tree in the yard.

" Oh, Mother ! May I have a puppy ? " said David. " It is what I want more than anything else in the world. I know where I can buy a real puppy with my dollar."

" Yes, David, I think a puppy is just what this family needs," said Mother.

Grandmother and Grandfather Turner said they thought so, too.

So after dinner Mother, Grandmother, and David got into the car. They went back to the house where the dogs lived.

David gave his shiny dollar to the man. Then David picked out the puppy he liked best. It was the black one with the white paw and the short tail.

David sat on the floor of the car with his puppy all the way home.

"David, does your puppy have a name?" asked Grandfather.

"No, he does not," said David. Then all at once he shouted, "But I know what I'll call him. I bought him with my shiny silver dollar, so I'll call him Dollar."

Mother and Grandmother thought Dollar was a fine name for the little dog.

That night David and Dollar sat on the front steps. They were waiting for Father to come from the city.

In a little while they saw Father's car turn into the yard. David and Dollar ran and met Father as he jumped out of the car.

251

"I bought a puppy with my dollar," said David. "His name is going to be Dollar. He is what I wanted more than anything else in the world!"

Dollar was glad that he had a fine new home! He was so glad that he had a little boy to play with that he ran around and around the yard.

David picked up Dollar, and up the front steps they went with Father.

"Good for David!" shouted Father. "Good for David and his new dog, Dollar."

252

How a Puppy Grows

I think it's very funny
The way a puppy grows—
A little on his wiggle-tail,
A little on his nose,
A little on his tummy
And a little on his ears;
I guess he'll be a dog all right
In half a dozen years.

Leroy F. Jackson

253

To the Teacher

Second Reader, Level II, *Around the Corner*, follows *We Are Neighbors*, the Second Reader, Level I, of the GINN BASIC READING SERIES. This Second Reader is designed to be read during the latter half of the second grade.

This Second Reader introduces 223 new words. The 326 words taught in the first-grade level of this series and the 226 words of the Second Reader, Level I, are repeated and maintained in this book. All variants of known words are counted as new with these exceptions: possessives and the plural *s* and *es* forms of nouns; the addition of *s*, *es*, *ed*, and *ing* to known verbs when there is no change in the spelling of the basic word; compounds where each part is known and contractions in which the apostrophe represents the omission of one letter.

The lines in the list indicate the ending of one story or unit and the beginning of another.

New Words in This Book

UNIT I

7. . . . .

---

8. . . . .
9. . . . .
10. . . . .
11. follow
12. . . . .

---

13. basement
empty
14. fine
15. Tony
peanut
16. . . . .
17. rattle
lunch
18. . . . .

---

19. elevator

20. bounce
21. . . . .
22. floor
stairs

---

23. Chris
apartment
24. bark
25. waited
26. Spring
27. . . . .
28. busy
own
29. . . . .
30. because

---

31. . . . .
32. fourth
33. stories
34. . . . .

35. family

---

36. *Poem*

UNIT II

37. circus

---

38. Casey
joins
39. lions
tents
40. blow
storm
41. tall
same
42. field
nearby
43. keep
small

---

44. ticket
roar
45. cotton
candy
46. once
clown
47. pink
48. waved

---

49. suits
trick
50. face
funniest
51. policeman
hair
52. head
53. . . . .
54. . . . .

254

55. country
beans
56. hay
roof
57. lumber
shed
58. use
59. blew
60. glad
61. . . .

62. *Poem*

UNIT III
63. . . .

64. tried
park
65. baseball
glove
66. seen
67. loud
high
68. began
thump
69. . . .

70. . . .
71. ground
72. behind
rode
73. . . .
74. real
hold

75. *Poem*

76. rows
moved
77. . . .
78. past
shop
79. grass
goldfish
80. . . .
81. different

82. bright
knew

83. Oscar
peep
84. smell
threw
85. quick
flash
86. brought
87. I'll
88. . . .

89. Abel
90. . . .
91. suppose
grow
92. seeds
crow
93. . . .
94. left
purple
95. well
squash
96. . . .
97. . . .
98. show
99. radio
100. . . .

UNIT IV
101. . . .

102. Andy
pilot
103. straight
ahead
104. . . .
105. . . .
106. sky
dark
107. oil
leak

108. tape
pipe
109. . . .

110. co-pilot
piles
111. smoke
low
112. burn
113. wife
say
114. flies

115. ranch
116. wind
117. sound
118. flat
land
119. . . .
120. supper

121. giant
Fellow
122. job
great
123. done
124. . . .
125. . . .

126. Hoppy
helicopter
127. jet
kind
128. silver
129. canyons
130. ladder
rope
131. need

132. *Poem*

UNIT V
133. . . .

134. shopkeeper

135. castle
through
136. cried
137. . . .

138. beanstalk
sell
139. food
140. hungry
141. might
142. hole
lay
143. . . .
144. treasures
145. harp
146. fell

147. rain-maker
dry
148. summer
149. secret
150. pay
151. river
152. tiny
153. . . .

154. *Poem*

155. Thumb
thistle
156. reach
mouth
157. . . .
158. cart
such
159. . . .
160. . . .

UNIT VI
161. . . .

162. Bushy
chipmunk
163. woods
while

255

ILLUSTRATIONS BY Edward Bradford, Robert Candy, Pru Herric, Hazel Hoecker, Bruce Howson, Ray Quigley, Catherine Scholz, Marguerite Scott, Fred Scott-Wood, Martha Setchell, Ralph Crosby Smith.

PRINTED IN THE UNITED STATES OF AMERICA